THE

FIELD MANUAL

FOR

THE USE OF THE OFFICERS

ON

ORDNANCE DUTY.

Reprinted from the 1862 edition
New material Copyright 1984 Dean S. Thomas
P.O. Box 3031
Gettysburg, PA 17325

Printed in the United States of America

THE

FIELD MANUAL

FOR

THE USE OF THE OFFICERS

ON

ORDNANCE DUTY.

PREPARED BY THE ORDNANCE BUREAU

RICHMOND:

PRINTED BY RITCHIE & DUNNAVANT.

1862.

ACKNOWLEDGEMENTS

My sincere thanks to the following individuals and institutions who helped to make this project possible:

Tom Dickey	Milwaukee Public Museum
Beverly DuBose	Museum of the Confederacy
Al Flickinger	Russ Pritchard
Paul Klatt	U.S. Army Military History Institute
Lewis Leigh, Jr.	Virginia Historical Society
Ben Michel	Terry White
	Russ Yeagy

The cannons depicted on Plates 3, 4, 5, 6, and 7 were photographed on the Gettysburg National Military Park by Dean S. Thomas.

INTRODUCTION

The Field Manual for the use of Officers on Ordnance Duty, prepared by the Confederate Ordnance Bureau in 1862, is rather unique when compared to other contemporary Confederate imprints. Unlike *The Ordnance Manual* and the *Ordnance Regulations* which were almost verbatum copies of their northern counterparts, *The Field Manual* presents a fresh look at Confederate ordnance materials. Although there are certain sections borrowed from J.G. Benton's *Ordnance and Gunnery*, and *The Ordnance Manual*, this volume contains a wealth of original information. It can be viewed as the way things were, rather than ought to be.

By 1862, the initial frenzied demands for gunpowder, weapons, ammunition, and the like were subsiding. Josiah Gorgas was organizing his C.S. Ordnance Department—John W. Mallet was named Superintendent of Laboratories in May (although not confirmed until October) and James H. Burton was appointed Superintendent of Armories in September. According to the commander of the Fayetteville Arsenal, blockade runners with their imported cargoes entered the port of Wilmington, N.C., "with the regularity of packets." Important manufacturing and ordnance facilities at Nashville, Tenn., and New Orleans, La., fell to Yankee advances, but on the whole the arsenal system was intact and beginning to work to its potential. The need to standardize products, and to describe the various ordnance stores for the many volunteer officers, led to the production of this booklet.

This reprint has been enhanced by the inclusion of over 100 photographs depicting much of the material described herein. Other "improvements" have been the addition of a hard cover and a Table of Contents. Otherwise the manual is complete in original form and awaits your enjoyment.

TABLE OF CONTENTS

ERRATA.

Page 7, line 7, for "Bumford" read "Bomford."

11, line 6 from bottom, for "125° to 300°" read "not less than 125°."

20, lines 5 and 14 from bottom, for "bands" read "lands."

20, line 9 from bottom, add "and is rifled with one turn in 16 feet."

21, line 7, for "twenty-seven" read "twenty-four."

23, line 10, after "dispensed with," add "with cast iron balls sulphur is used."

24, line 8, for ".2607" read ".2607 lbs."

36, line 5, for "0.75" read ".075."

37, line 22, for "plane" read "line."

53, line 25, for ".36 inch" read ".37 inch."

54, line 6, for "band" read "barrel."

56, line 14, for "the size above mentioned" read "48 in. by 14 in. weighing 4 lbs."

74, line 8 from bottom, for "thin" read "three."

76 (table), weight of 6-pdr. spherical case, for "2.5 lbs." read "5.5 lbs."

THE

FIELD MANUAL

FOR

THE USE OF THE OFFICERS

ON

ORDNANCE DUTY.

PREPARED BY THE ORDNANCE BUREAU

RICHMOND:

PRINTED BY RITCHIE & DUNNAVANT.

1862.

FIELD MANUAL

CHAP. I.

ORDNANCE.

Ordnance for the *land service* is made chiefly by private contractors, under the direction of officers of the Ordnance Bureau. The kinds and calibres used are as follows:

KIND OF ORDNANCE.		CALIBRE.	MATERIAL.	MODEL.
GUNS.	Mountain rifle, . .	2.25-inch, . . .	Bronze, .	1862
		3-inch (rifled), .	Cast iron,	1861
	Field, ...	6-pounder, . . .	Bronze, .	1841
		12 pounder, . .	" .	1841
		12-pounder, . .	" .	Napoleon.
	Siege and garrison,	4.62-inch (rifled),	Cast iron,	1862
		12-pounder, . .	"	1839
		18-pounder, . .	" .	1839
		24-pounder, . .	" .	1839
	Seacoast, ...	32-pounder, . .	" .	1841
		42-pounder, . .	" .	1841
COLUMBIADS, ...		8-inch, ...	" .	1844
		8-inch, ...	"	1861
		10-inch, ...	" .	1844
		10-inch, ...	"	1861
		15-inch, ...	"	1862
HOWITZERS.	Mountain, ...	12-pounder, . .	Bronze, . .	1841
	Field, ...	12-pounder, . .	Iron, . .	1862
		12-pounder, . .	Bronze, .	1841
		24-pounder, . .	"	1844
	Garrison and siege,	24-pounder, . .	Cast iron,	1841
		8-inch, ...	" .	1841
	Seacoast, . . .	8-inch, ...	" .	1841
		10-inch, ...	" .	1841
MORTARS.	Siege, ...	8-inch, ...	" .	1841
		10-inch, ...	" .	1844
	Seacoast, ...	10-inch, ...	" .	1841
		13-inch, ...	" .	1841
	Coehorn, ...	24-pounder, . .	Bronze, .	1841

There are in some of the forts guns of an older model than the above. The 42-pounder gun and the 8 and 10 inch seacoast howitzers are suppressed by order of Feb. 9th, 1861. Some of the 8 and 10 inch columbiads have been rifled; the first to a calibre of 5.8 inch; the second, 6.4 inch. Their frequent bursting has caused this class of rifled guns to be discontinued. A few of the 8 inch siege howitzers were also rifled, for experiment, with a bore of 4.62 inch.

Guns and howitzers take their denominations from the weights of their solid shot in round numbers, including the 42-pounder; large pieces, rifle guns and mortars, from the diameter of the bore.

DEFINITIONS.

Cascable.—The knob on the end of the breech of a gun; it is composed of the *knob* and *neck;* sometimes the *fillet.*

Breech.—The mass of solid metal behind the bottom of the bore, extending to the cascable.

Base of the breech.—The rear surface of the breech.

Base line.—A line traced round the gun in rear of the vent.

Base ring.—A projecting band of metal adjoining the base of the breech, and connected with the body of the gun by a concave moulding.

Reinforce.—The thickest part of the body of the gun, in front of the base ring or line: if there is more than one reinforce, that which is next to the base ring is called the *first reinforce;* the other the *second reinforce.*

Reinforce band.—A band at the junction of the first and second reinforces.

Chase.—The conical part of the gun in front of the reinforce.

Astragal and fillets.—The moulding at the front end of the chase.

Chase ring.—A band at the front end of the chase.

Neck.—The smallest part of the piece, in front of the chase.

Swell of the muzzle.—The largest part of the gun in front of the neck.

Muzzle band.—A band which takes the place of the swell of the muzzle in some guns.

Face of the piece.—The plane terminating the gun at the muzzle.

Trunnions.—Two cylinders, near the centre of gravity of the gun, by which it is supported on its carriage. The axes of the trunnions are in a line perpendicular to the bore, and in our guns, in the same plane with the axis.

Rimbase.—The shoulder at the base of the trunnions.

Bore.—All the part bored out, including the chamber and the junction of the bore with the chamber.

Chamber.—The small part of some bores; it contains the charge of powder.

Gomer chamber.—A conical chamber which is joined to the cylinder of the bore by a portion of a spherical surface.

True windage.—The difference between the true diameters of the bore and of the ball.

Lock piece.—A block of metal at the outer opening of the vent to facilitate attaching a lock to the gun.

Natural line of sight.—A line drawn in a vertical plane through the axis of the piece from the highest point of the base ring to the highest point of the swell of the muzzle, or to the top of the sight, if there be one.

Natural angle of sight.—The angle which the natural line of sight makes with the axis of the piece.

Dispart.—The difference of the semi-diameters of the base ring and the swell of the muzzle, or the muzzle band. It is therefore the tangent of the natural angle of sight to a radius equal to the distance from the rear of the base ring to the highest point of the swell of the muzzle, the sight, or the front of the muzzle band, as the case may be.

Preponderance.—The excess of weight of the part in rear of the trunnions over that in front; it is measured by the weight which the breech bears on a balance, the point of support resting at the rear of the base ring, at the base line, or at the bottom of the ratchet, the gun being suspended freely on the axis of the trunnions.

Handles.—Flat rings cast on some bronze pieces; they are placed with their centres over the centre of gravity of the piece.

Ear.—A lug of metal cast on some mortars; it is attached to a *clevis* by a bolt, and constitutes a handle.

NOMENCLATURE.

Guns of the Model of 1861.

Parts.—The *bore*, a cylinder terminated by *curved surfaces*, the *chamber*. The *breech ;* the *cascable*, the *knob*, the *neck*. The *body of the gun ;* the *reinforce*, the *chase*, the *muzzle*, the *face*, the *trunnions*, the *rimbases*.

Mouldings.—None.

Columbiads.—Add to the above the *ratchet*, the *sight-piece*.

The vent is in the vertical plane of the axis, *perpendicular to it*, and enters the bore at the termination of the cylinder of the bore, or slightly in front of it.

Guns of the Model of 1841–44.

The general difference between guns of the model of 1861 and of 1841–44, is, that in the latter the vent makes an angle of 80° with the axis of the bore, entering the bore one-fourth diameter of the bore from the bottom, and that the latter have more mouldings. In the model of 1861, all unnecessary *mouldings* are dispensed with, as they are found to materially injure the strength of the gun.

DIFFERENT KINDS OF CANNON.

Gun.—A gun, technically, is a heavy cannon, intended to throw solid shot with large charges of powder. It may be distinguished from other cannon by its great weight and length, and by the absence of a chamber.

Howitzer.—The howitzer is a cannon employed to throw large hollow projectiles with comparatively small charges of powder. It is shorter, lighter, and more cylindrical in shape than a gun of the same calibre, and it has a cylindrical chamber for the reception of powder. The chief advantage of a howitzer over a gun is, that with less weight of piece it can produce at short ranges a greater effect.

Mortar.—A mortar is a short cannon used to throw large hollow projectiles at great angles of elevation—usually that of 45°. It has a chamber generally of a conical form.

Columbiad.—The columbiad combines certain qualities of the gun, howitzer, and mortar. It is a long (the model of 1841-44 having a cylindrical chamber), heavy piece, capable of projecting shot and shells, with heavy charges of powder, at high angles of elevation. Invented by Col. Bumford, and used for solid shot in 1812.

Carronade.—A carronade is a light cannon about 6 calibres long in the bore, weighing about 65 times the weight of the projectile. It was formerly much used on ships of war. A carronade has no trunnions, but is supported on its carriage by a stout bolt, which passes through a loop cast on the under side. Its name is derived from the *Carron* foundry, where they were first made. It is not used in the C. S. service.

Rifle cannon.—These are of a recent date, and are distinguished from the smooth bore, in having *the rifles* or threads of a female screw cut in the bore. There are many varieties.

CHAMBERS.

Experience shows that up to a charge of powder equal to one-seventh of the weight of the projectile, and a length of bore equal to 9 or 10 calibres, a chamber is advantageous; but beyond these limits, it possesses no compensating advantages.

There are three kinds of chambers used in fire arms: *cylindrical, conical,* or *spherical.*

Cylindrical chamber.—This is a cylinder of smaller diameter than the bore, terminated at bottom by a portion of a sphere, and connected, by a spherical or a conical surface, with the bore. For very small charges of powder and short lengths of bore, the cylindrical chamber gives better results than the conical. Hence, all howitzers are provided with the cylindrical chamber.

Conical chamber.—This, called also the *Gomer* chamber, consists of the frustrum of a cone connected with the bore by a portion of the surface of a sphere. This kind of chamber is considered the most advantageous for large charges, and is adopted in mortars.

Spherical chamber.—This consists of a sphere joined to the bore of the piece by means of a small cylinder, which serves as a channel to the gases. It is now entirely abandoned.

Grooves of the Rifled Gun.

Number of grooves, -	4.62-inch rifled guns,			7
	3 " " "			5
Width, - - -	4.62 " " "			0.5 inch.
	3 " " "			0.4 "
Depth, - - -	4.62 " " "			0.1 "
	3 " " "			0.07 "
Twist, - - -	4.62 " " "	1 turn in 19	feet.
	3 ". " "	1 " in 14	"
Width of lands, - -	4.62 " " "			1.87 inch.
	3 " " "			1.5 "

TO DESIGNATE A PIECE OF ORDNANCE.

State the kind, the calibre (in inches if it be foreign ordnance), the material, the weight, the inspector's initials, the number, the country in which it was made, the date, the place of fabrication, the founder's name, the name inscribed on it, its condition for service, the kind of chamber, if any; whether it has a vent piece, a lock piece, handles, the ornaments, and any particular marks which may serve to identify it.

PRINCIPAL DIMENSIONS AND WEIGHTS OF SIEGE AND FIELD GUNS.

	IRON				BRONZE		
	SIEGE.	FIELD (model '62).		MOUNTAIN		FIELD.	
	24-pr.	6-pr.	3-in. rifle.	2.25-in. rifle.	12-pr.	12-pr. Napoleon.	6-pr.
	Inches.	Inches.	Inches.	Inches.	Inches.	Inches.	Inches.
Diameter of the bore,	5.82	3.67	3.	2.25	4.62	4.62	3.67
True windage,	0.14	0.10	0.05	0.05	0.10	0.10	0.09
Length of bore,	108.	62.45	62.5	40.	74.	63.6	57.5
Ditto, in diameters,	18.56	16.74	20.83	17.7	16.	13.76	15.67
Length from rear of base ring to face of muzzle,	114.	61.95	62.	40.87	78.	66.	60.
Whole length of the piece,	124.	70.71	72.	44.	85.	72.15	65.6.
Semi-diameter of the base ring,	10.7	5.75	5.25	3.	6.5	5.5	5.15
Semi-diameter of the swell of the muzzle,	7.793	–	–	–	5.17	4.25	4.125
Distance between these two semi-diameters,	111.	–	–	–	76.3	65.	58.7
Natural angle of sight,	1° 30′	2° 45′	2° 45′	1° 45′	1°	1° 6′	1°
Distance from rear of base ring to rear of trunnions,	43.	19.115	19.165	16.38	30.7	25.4	23.25
Diameter of the base ring,	21.4	11.5	11.5	6.	13.	11.	10.3
Distance between the rimbases,	18.	9.5	9.5	6.9	12.	11.5	9.5
Length of the trunnions,	5.	2.75	2.75	2.25	3.5	3.25	2.8
Diameter of the trunnions,	5.82	3.67	3.67	2.7	4.62	4.2	3.67
Distance from axis of trunnions to face of muzzle,	68.09	41.	41.	23.25	44.99	38.5	34.91
Weight, pounds,	5,790	967	967	200	1,757	1,227	884•
Preponderance, pounds,	395	75	75	30	108	123	47

PRINCIPAL DIMENSIONS AND WEIGHTS OF SIEGE AND FIELD HOWITZERS.

	IRON			BRONZE			
	SIEGE.		FIELD (Model '62.)	FIELD.			MOUNTAIN.
	8-inch.	24-pdr.	12-pdr.	32-pdr.	24-pdr.	12-pdr.	12-pdr.
	Inches.	Inches.	Inches.	Inches.	Inches.	Inches.	Inches.
Diameter of the bore,	8.	5.82	4.62	6.4	5.82	4.62	4.62
True windage,	0.12	0.14	0.12	0.15	0.14	0.10	0.10
Length of bore, exclusive of chamber,	38.5	53.25	48.8	64.	56.25	46.25	28.16
" " " in diam.	4.81	9.15	12.13	10.	9.66	10.	6.1
Diameter of the chamber,	4.62	4.62	3.67	4.62	4.62	3.67	3.34
Length of the chamber,	8.	4.75	7.	7.	4.75	4.25	2.75
Length from rear of base ring to face of muzzle,	52.	62.	56.	75.	65.	53.	32.91
Whole length of the piece,	61.5	69.	64.4	82.	71.2	58.6	37.21
Semi-diameter of base ring,	9.125	6.9	5.3	6.9	6.	5.	3.8
Semi-diameter of swell of muzzle,	8.225	5.85	–	5.6	4.875	4.1	3.45
Distance between these semi-diameters,	51.5	61.8	–	74.75	64.8	52.85	32.91
Natural angle of sight,	1°	1°	–	1°	1°	1°	0° 37'
Dist. from rear of base ring to rear of trunnions,	24.	24.69	24.21	30.7	27.5	23.25	15.
Diameter of base ring,	18.25	13.8	10.6	13.8	12.	10.	7.6
Distance between the rimbases,	18.	12.8	9.6	12.	11.5	9.5	6.9
Length of the trunnions,	.5	3.25	3.	3.5	3.25	2.8	2.25
Diameter of the trunnions,	5.82	4.62	3.67	4.62	4.2	3.67	2.7
Dist. from axis of trunnions to face of muzzle,	25.09	35.	31.3	41.99	35.4	27.91	16.56
Weight, pounds,	2,614	1,476	850	1,920	1,318	788	220
Preponderance, pounds,	420	70	75	160	146	95	

MATERIALS FOR ORDNANCE.

Bronze.

Bronze for cannon (commonly called *brass*) consists of 90 parts of copper, and 10 of tin, allowing a variation of one part of tin, more or less. It is more fusible than copper, much less so than tin, more sonorous, harder, and less susceptible of oxidation, and much less ductile than either of its components. Its fracture is of a yellowish color, with little lustre, a coarse grain, irregular, and often exhibiting spots of tin, which are of a whitish color. These spots indicate defects in the metal; but they seldom contain more than 25 per cent. of tin. The specific gravity of bronze is about 8,700, being greater than the mean of the specific gravities of copper and tin.

Pure copper is of a red color, inclining to yellow; it has a fine metallic lustre. Its fracture exhibits a short, even, close grain, of a silky appearance; it is very ductile and very malleable. The greater the purity of copper, the more malleable it is, and the finer the grain. Specific gravity from 8,600 to 9,000.

Pure tin is of a white color, a little darker than silver; it is malleable, and susceptible of being rolled into sheets, but it is not very ductile; it is very soft, and when bent backwards and forwards, it gives a peculiar crackling sound, the distinctness of which is in proportion to the purity of the tin. Specific gravity, 7,290 to 7,320.

Cast Iron.

Iron for making cannon should be smelted with the greatest possible care, with charcoal, and a blast of a constant temperature of 125° to 300°, depending upon the ore used. All the materials which enter the smelting furnace should be of the best and purest quality. The most important quality of gun-iron, after a medium strength of 25,000 to 30,000 pounds per square inch, is *uniformity*, without which no two guns can be made alike, or any idea formed of what kind of guns are being made. The essential qualities of good gun-iron, are tenacity, elasticity, extensibility and incompressibility: that iron will be the best which has them all in the greatest degree, and the absence of any one will render the iron unfit for guns.

Before making guns from an iron which has never been tried for this purpose, a sample-gun of the calibre of the gun to be made, should first endure a satisfactory proof with service charges. The mean specific gravity of gun-iron is about 7,248, and the average tenacity about 30,000 pounds per square inch.

Wrought Iron and Steel.

Experimental guns have been made of wrought iron and steel, giving satisfactory results, and an order has been given for guns, to be made of the former material. The superior strength of these materials, and the evenness, smoothness and hardness of surface of which they are susceptible, render it probable that these are the materials of which our field rifle guns will soon be exclusively made.

MARKS.

All cannon are required to be weighed, and to be marked as follows, viz: the *number of the gun*, and *the initials of the inspector's name*, on the face of the muzzle; the numbers in a separate series for each kind and calibre at each foundry; the initial letters of the *name of the founder* and of the foundry, on the end of the right trunnion; the *year of fabrication* on the end of the left trunnion; the *foundry number* on the end of the right rimbase, above the trunnion; the *weight of the piece in pounds* on the base of the breech; the letters C. S. on the upper surface of the piece, near the end of the reinforce.

Cannon rejected on inspection are marked X C on the face of the muzzle; if condemned for erroneous dimensions which cannot be remedied, add X D; if by powder proof, X P; if by water proof, X W.

INJURIES CAUSED BY SERVICE.

Brass cannon are little subject to external injury, except from the bending of the trunnions sometimes after long service or heavy charges.

Internal injuries are caused by the action of the elastic fluids developed in the combustion of the powder, or by the action of the shot in passing out of the bore. These effects generally increase with the calibre of the piece.

Of the first kind, which exhibit themselves in rear of the shot, are: *The enlargement of the bore* by the compression of the metal, which is seldom a serious defect; *corrosion of metal*, particularly at the angles, such as the inner orifice of the vent, or the mouth of a cylindrical chamber; *cracks*, from the yielding of the cohesion of the metal; *cavities*, cracks enlarged by the action of the gas, and by the melting of the metal; observable especially in the upper surface of the bore.

Injuries of the second kind, which appear in front of the charge, are: *The lodgment of the shot*, a compression of the metal on the lower side of the bore, at the seat of the shot, caused by the pressure of the fluid in escaping over the top of the shot. There is a corresponding *burr* in front of the lodgment, and the motion thereby given to the shot causes it to strike alternately on the top and bottom of the bore, producing other *enlargements*, generally *three* in number; it is chiefly from this cause that bronze guns become unserviceable. *Scratches*, caused by the fragments of a broken shot, or the roughness of an imperfect one.

The durability of bronze guns may be much increased by careful use, and by the precautions of *increasing the length of the cartridge*, or that of the *sabot*, or using *a wad over the cartridge*, in order to change the place of the shot; by *wrapping the shot in woolen or other cloth*, or in paper, so as to diminish the windage and the bounding of the shot in the bore. The French bronze siege guns, which formerly were rendered unserviceable in 600 service rounds, now endure by this method 2,500 service rounds. In field *guns*, both bronze and iron, the paper cap, which is taken off from the cartridge, should always be *put over the shot*.

Iron guns are subject to the above defects in a less degree than bronze, except from corrosion of the metal. The principal cause of injury to iron guns is *rusting* of the metal, producing a roughness and enlargement of the bore.

The service to which an iron gun has been subjected, may generally be determined by the appearance of the vent. This is examined by taking a cast of it in lead. After about 500 rounds, the vent becomes enlarged to .3 inch, and should not be longer used.

In rifled guns, the wear of the vent is about twice as great as in smooth bored guns.

Replacing vents.—In bronze field pieces, the vent piece is taken out and a new one screwed in. In other guns, the vent is filled up by pouring in melted zinc, the vent being closed on the interior by means of clay placed on the head of a rammer, and pressed against the upper surface of the bore, and a new vent is bored at a distance of two or three inches from the first.

Spiking and unspiking Guns, and rendering them unserviceable.

To spike a piece, or to render it unserviceable.—Drive into the vent a jagged and hardened steel spike with a soft point, or a nail without a head; break it off flush with the outer surface, and clinch the point inside by means of a rammer. Wedge a shot in the bottom of the bore by wrapping it with felt, or by means of iron wedges, using the rammer, or a bar of iron to drive them in; a wooden wedge would be easily burnt by means of a charcoal fire, lighted with the aid of a bellows. Cause shells to burst in the bore of bronze guns, or fire broken shot from them with high charges. Fill a piece with sand over the charge to burst it. Fire a piece against another, muzzle to muzzle, or the muzzle of one to the chase of the other. Light a fire under the chase of a bronze gun, and strike on it with a sledge to bend it. Break off the trunnions of iron guns; or burst them by firing them with heavy charges, and full of shot at a high elevation. When guns are to be spiked temporarily, and are likely to be retaken, a *spring spike* is used, having a shoulder to prevent its being too easily extracted.

To unspike a piece.—If the spike is not screwed in or clinched, and the bore is not impeded, put in a charge of powder of one-third the weight of the shot, and ram junk wads over it with a handspike, laying on the bottom of the bore a strip of wood with a groove on the under side, containing a strand of quick-match, by which fire is communicated to the charge; in a bronze gun, take out some of the metal at the upper orifice of the vent and pour sulphuric acid into the groove for some hours before firing. If this method, several times repeated, is not successful, unscrew the vent piece if it be a bronze gun, and if an iron one, drill out the spike, or drill a new vent.

To drive out a shot wedged in the bore.—Unscrew the vent piece, if there be one, and drive in wedges so as to start the shot forward—then ram it back again, in order to seize the wedge with a hook; or pour in powder and fire it after replacing the vent piece. In the last resort bore a hole in the bottom of the breech, drive out the shot and stop the hole with a screw.

To use a piece which has been spiked.—Insert one end of a piece of quick-match in the cartridge, allowing the other to project out of the muzzle of the gun. Apply the fire to the quick-match, and get out of the way. When quick-match of sufficient length is not at hand, insert one end in the cartridge, the other projecting in front of the shot; and after ramming the cartridge home, throw two or three pinches of powder into the bore. Place another piece of match in the muzzle, the end projecting out. The piece may be fired in this way without danger. Quick-match in the cartridge may be dispensed with by piercing three or four holes in the cartridge bag. In this manner the gun may be fired with great rapidity.

PRESERVATION OF ORDNANCE.

Cannon should be placed together, according to kind and calibre, on skids of stone, iron, or wood, laid on hard ground, well rammed and covered with a layer of cinders, or of some other material, to prevent vegetation.

Guns and long howitzers.—The pieces should rest on the skids in front of the base ring and in rear of the astragal; the axis inblined at an angle of 4 or 5 degrees with the horizon, the muzzle lowest; the trunnions touching each other; or if space is wanting for that arrangement, the trunnion of one piece may rest on the adjoining piece, so that the axis of the trunnions is inclined about 45° with a horizontal line; the vent down, stopped with a greased wooden plug, or with putty or tallow. If circumstances require it, the pieces may be piled in two tiers, with skidding placed between them, exactly over those which rest on the ground; the muzzles of both tiers in the same direction and their axes preserving the same inclination.

Short howitzers and mortars.—On thick planks, standing on their muzzles, the trunnions touching, the vents stopped.

Iron ordnance should be covered on the exterior with a lacker impervious to water; the bore and the vent should be greased with a mixture of *oil* and *tallow*, or of *tallow* and *beeswax* melted together and boiled to expel the water. The lacker should be renewed as often as requisite, and the grease at least once every year.

The lacker and grease should be applied in hot weather.

The cannon should be frequently inspected, to see that moisture does not collect in the bore.

History of Cannon.

Gunpowder became generally known in Europe about 1320, and about this time it was first used to project rounded stones from short conical guns, made in the shape of an apothecary's mortar.

Perrieres.—These were succeeded by guns made of long and cylindrical bars of iron bound together by hoops, with a chamber for the powder, called *perrieres*, from being used to breach stone walls.

Culverin.—The introduction of the cast iron instead of the stone projectile, caused the rejection of the *perrieres* for the *culverin*, a gun somewhat like that used at present, of cast metal, only much longer bore, and ornamented on the exterior with various devices. There is one now at Dover, England, 25 feet long, which casts a projectile of 18 pounds, called "Queen Anne's Pocket Piece."

Breech-loading cannon.—In the repository at Woolwich, there is a gun marked 1426, with a moveable breech. Among the earliest cannon are found those loading at the breech. They were soon abandoned for want of strength.

Arquebuse.—The *arquebuse* was a light gun, to be used by the hand, which came into use about 1524; and this was finally succeeded by the musket, cannon having been in use nearly two hundred years before the musket.

Ancient mortars.—In 1478 an attempt was made to use hollow projectiles, to which was attached a burning match, but with little success. In 1634 the present *mortars* were introduced in the French service.

Ancient howitzers.—Early attempts were also made to throw hollow projectiles from the long *culverins;* but the difficulty of loading, as the match was lighted before they were introduced, caused the attempt to be abandoned, until the Dutch artillerists conceived the idea of reducing its length so the projectile could be readily inserted. These cannon, thus reduced, came into general use, under the name of *Howitzers* from the German, *Haubitz.*

Calibres.—The principal series were the French: the 32-pounder, 16-pounder, 8-pounder, 4-pounder and 2-pounder; and the German, the 48-pounder, 24-pounder, 12-pounder, 6-pounder, 3-pounder and 1½-pounder. To one or the other of these, all the various systems of calibres were finally reduced.

Valiere.—In 1732 Gen. Valiere established a system of uniformity for cannon throughout France. Still, the carriages for different calibres were of different dimensions; the axletrees were of wood, and gun carriages without limbers.

Gribeauval.—In 1765 Gen. Gribeauval effected the most important changes in artillery. He diminished the charge of powder from one-half to one-third the weight of the ball, and was thereby enabled to make the gun lighter; he disposed the horses in double file, having been previously arranged in single; he introduced iron axletrees, cartridges instead of loose powder, elevating screws and tangent scales, and compelled all the arsenals to make the work according to fixed dimensions.

Afterwards, all field carriages were reduced to two, making the wheels of the limber and of the carriage the same, and an ammunition chest placed on the limber. The two flasks which formed the trail, were replaced by a single piece, called the *stock*, allowing the piece to turn in a smaller space.

Napoleon gun.—In 1850 the present Emperor of France substituted a single gun of medium weight and 12 lbs. calibre, capable of firing both shot and shell, for the 8 and 12-pounder guns, and 24 and 32-pounder howitzers then in use. It is also called *canon-obusier*, or gun-howitzer. All the field batteries in the French service in the Crimean war, consisted of these Napoleon guns, each drawn by eight horses. This gun is now adopted in the C. S. service.

Increase in calibre.—In 1830 the heaviest gun mounted in the U. S. service, was a 42-pounder; now, 15-inch columbiads, casting a ball of 400 lbs. weight, and mortars, throwing 15-inch shell of 320 lbs. weight, are in use.

Rifle cannon.—The first *rifled* small arm is said to have been made in 1498; yet the method of *rifling* was not applied to cannon until a recent period. Col. Cavalli of the Sardinian service introduced about 1832 a *breech-loading* rifle cannon, which was somewhat noted, though not generally adopted.

Lancaster gun.—During the Crimean war Mr. Lancaster introduced his rifle cannon of elliptical bore. It was like a smooth bore with its section an ellipse instead of a circle; having the major axis of the ellipse at the muzzle at right angles to the major axis at the breech. They wholly failed, at the siege of Sevastopol, to realize the expectations formed, and from frequent bursting, were finally discarded.

Rifle field pieces were first used with great effect by the French in the Italian war, and *rifle siege pieces* have been first used in the present war.

Among the most celebrated *rifle cannon*, are the *Armstrong*, the *Whitworth* and the *Parrott*. Some of these are now in the C. S. service, obtained either by capture or purchase.

The Armstrong gun, so called from the inventor, who was knighted by the English government for the invention, is a breech-loading rifle cannon, made of wrought iron tubes welded together; each tube is from two to three feet long, and is formed by twisting a square bar of iron around a mandrel, and welding the edges together, as a good fowling piece is made. In the rear of the trunnions it is enveloped with two additional thicknesses of tubes. The outer consists of a spiral coil, but the inner is formed of an iron slab bent into a circular shape and welded. This intermediate layer has chiefly to sustain the pressure on the bottom of the bore.

Breech.—The breech is closed with a vent piece, which is slipped with the hand into a slot cut into the breech of the piece, and held in its place by a breech screw, which supports it from behind. This screw is made in the form of a tube, so that its hollow forms a part of the bore prolonged, when the vent piece is withdrawn: and through this hollow tube the charge is passed into the chamber.

Bore.—The bore of the field gun is three inches in diameter, and is rifled with thirty-four narrow grooves. Twist, one turn in 9 feet.

Projectile.—It consists of a very thin cast iron shell enclosing forty-two segment shaped pieces of cast iron built up so as to form a cylindrical cavity in the centre. The exterior of the shell is thinly coated with lead. The lead is also allowed to percolate among the segments so as to fill up the interstices, the central cavity being kept open by the insertion of a steel core. In this state the projectile is so compact that it may be fired through six feet of hard timber without injury; while its resistance to a bursting charge is so small that less than one ounce of powder is required to burst it.

The gun can be fired with great rapidity, and apparently for any length of time, without being sponged. The Armstrong gun always throws to the right, increasing with the range. This constant deviation or "drift" is allowed for by a lateral motion of the rear sight.

Eight degrees of elevation give a range of about 3,000 yards. In connection with the elevating apparatus, the field carriage has a *lateral screw* for giving a slight transverse motion to the piece in pointing. None of them are in the C. S. service.

The Whitworth gun is a breech-loading rifle cannon, made of steel, with a wrought iron band at the breech. The breech screws off and works in a collar turning on a hinge. It is 100 inches long in the bore, which is somewhat hexagonal in form. The calibre of the inscribed circle is 2.71 inches. The sides of the hexagon have *one turn in 4½ feet*. The vent is in the direction of the axis of the bore. The projectile is a hexagonal prismoid in form, to fit the bore, with the front end a paraboloid. The carriage is provided with an azimuth screw of play of 1½ inch for moving the gun in azimuth. It derives its name from the celebrated English machinist Whitworth, its inventor, and is said to have a remarkable range. A few are in the C. S. service, by purchase.

The Parrott gun derives its name from its inventor, Mr. Parrott of New York. It is a cast iron rifle cannon, with the distinctive characteristic of being reinforced at the breech with a *wrought iron* band, and of having *grooves equal in width to the bands*. The groove is a portion of an annulus with rounded corners.

The Parrott (*called also* 10-*pounder rifled*) *gun* has a calibre 2.9 inches. Length from rear of base band to muzzle, 72.8 inches. Three grooves .05 inch deep, wrought iron band at breech 13 inches in length and 1.18 inch thick.

The 20-*pounder Parrott gun* (captured before Richmond) has a calibre of 3.67 inches; length from rear of base band to muzzle, 83 inches; wrought iron band at breech, 16 inches in length and 1.5 inch in thickness. It has *five* grooves equal to the bands in width, and is rifled with one turn in 24 feet.

The 30-*pounder Parrott gun* (captured at Manassas) has a calibre of 4.2 inches; weight 4190 lbs.; entire length 132 inches; five grooves. The wrought iron band at breech is 19 inches in length and 2 inches in thickness. It is rifled with one turn in 24 feet.

A few 3-inch guns have been rifled and banded at the Tredegar works like the Parrott gun. A few 3-inch wrought iron guns have also been captured. They are known by the outline being a continuous curve.

Austrian guns.—Twenty-seven bronze field pieces have been introduced into the C. S. service from Austria. *Seven* are 24-pounder howitzers, cast in Vienna, 1857-59, of calibre 5.87, instead of 5.82. The remaining seventeen are 6-pounders, cast in Vienna in 1826 and 1859, of calibre 3.74 instead of 3.67. By having the balls *enclosed in canvas*, the ordinary ammunition issued for the approximate calibres in the C. S. service may be used with these guns and howitzers.

The Blakeley gun derives its name from its maker, Mr. Blakeley of England. The field piece is a 12-pounder rifle cannon, of calibre 3.50 inches, with saw tooth grooves. Some are in service, obtained by purchase.

CHAP. II.

PROJECTILES.

MATERIAL.

Stone projectiles were used before the invention of gunpowder, and very generally after it, until the year 1400, when the French made them of cast iron. Until quite lately, bronze guns, throwing stone balls of enormous calibre, were used by the Turks in defending the passage of the Dardanelles.

Lead is too soft to be used against very resisting objects. Large projectiles are liable to be disfigured and partially melted by the violent shock and great heat of large charges of powder.

Wrought iron can be used when great strength and density are required. It is very expensive.

Cast iron unites, in a greater degree than any other material, the essential qualities of hardness, strength, density and cheapness.

Compound projectiles.—At the siege of Cadiz, cast iron projectiles, filled with lead, were used, combining thus great strength and density. For rifle guns, in some services, the projectiles are coated with lead. In the C. S. service a copper disc is used.

CLASSIFICATION.

Projectiles may be classified in *spherical* and *oblong*. The *spherical* are used in smooth bored guns, and the *oblong* in rifle guns. They are further classified according to their structure.

Solid or *round shot* are made of cast iron, and are used in *guns*.

Shells are *hollow shot* made of cast iron. For field guns and howitzers their calibres are expressed by the weight of the equivalent solid shot, as 12 and 24 pound shells; and for all other howitzers and mortars, by the diameter of the bore of the piece, as 8 and 10 inch shells. They have less strength to resist a shock, and are therefore fired with a smaller charge of powder than solid shot. The cavity contains a bursting charge of powder, or a bursting charge and incendiary composition, if the object be to destroy by combustion.

Spherical case shot were invented or perfected by Col. *Schrapnell* of the British army, and hence are often called "*Schrapnell*." They consist of thin cast iron shells filled with round musket balls. Formerly the interstices were filled with melted sulphur to solidify the mass, and a hole bored through the mass to receive the bursting charge. Now, by packing the balls in tight, the sulphur is dispensed with The 12-pounder spherical case shot contains about 90 bullets and a bursting charge of 1 oz. of powder, and the 24-pounder contains about 175 bullets.

Grape shot.—A grape shot is composed of *nine* small cast iron balls of a size appropriate to the calibre, disposed in three layers of three balls each. Formerly the balls were held together by a covering of canvas and a net-work of twine, called *quilted grape*. Now a *stand of grape* is held together by two rings and a plate at each end of the stand connected by a rod or bolt. Grape shot are used in all smooth bored guns except the *field* and *mountain* services.

Canister shot.—A canister shot is a *tin* cylinder with iron heads filled with balls packed in sawdust. The balls are all made of *cast iron*, except for the *mountain howitzer*. A canister shot for a *gun* contains 27 small balls arranged in 4 layers—the top of 6, and the remainder of 7 each. That for a *howitzer* contains 48 balls in four layers of 12 each. They are used in the field, mountain, siege and seacoast services.

Bar shot consist of two spheres connected by a bar of iron. They are very inaccurate—so much so as at the present to be abandoned.

Chain shot only differ from *bar shot* in the connection being by a chain instead of a bar.

Carcasses are shells having, besides the usual eye, three others, which are placed at equal distances apart, and tangent to the great circle of the shell, which is perpendicular to the axis of the first eye. They are filled with combustible composition, primed at the four holes with quick-match and mealed powder, and are used to set fire to an enemy's works, the additional holes being to allow a more rapid escape of the flame.

Grenades.—A *hand grenade* is a small shell thrown from the hand. *Rampart grenades* are larger, and are used to roll down a breach in its defence, to throw over the ramparts, &c. Six-pounder spherical case shot may be used as hand grenades.

SHOT.

Calibre, - -	32	24	18	12	9	6	4	3	1
Diameter, - - -	6.25	5.68	5.17	4.52	4.10	3.58	3.12	2.84	1.95
Weight, - - -	32.6	24.4	18.5	12.3	9.25	6.10	4.07	3.05	1.00

The specific gravity of shot and shell is about 7,000. Shells 7.1.

1-6 π D³ being the volume of a sphere, and .2607 the weight of a cubic inch of cast iron, the weight of a cast iron sphere will be 1-6 π D³ x .2607 $=$ 1-6 x 3.1416 x .2607 D³ $=$ 0.134 D³.

To find the weight of a cast iron shot or shell:

Multiply the cube of the diameter of the shot in inches, or the difference of the cubes of the exterior and interior diameters of the shell, by 0.134 for the weight in pounds.

For lead balls, the multiplier is 0.2142.

To find the diameter of a cast iron shot of a given weight:

Divide the weight in pounds by 0.134, and the cube root of the quotient will be the diameter in inches.

To find the quantity of powder which a shell will contain:

Multiply the cube of the interior diameter of the shell in inches by 0.01744, for the weight of powder in pounds.

To find the number of balls in a pile:

Multiply the sum of the three parallel edges by one-third of the number of balls in a triangular face.

In a square pile, one of the parallel edges contains but one ball; in a triangular pile, two of the edges have but one ball in each.

The number of balls in a triangular face is $\dfrac{n\,(n -\!- 1)}{2}$; *n* being the number in the bottom row.

The sum of the three parallel edges in a triangular pile is $n + 2$; in a square pile, $2n + 1$; in an oblong pile, $3N + 2n - 2$; N being the length of the top row, and n the width of the bottom tier; or, $3m - n + 1$; m being the length and n the width of the bottom tier.

If a pile consist of two piles joined at a right angle, calculate the contents of one as a common oblong pile, and of the other as a pile of which the three parallel edges are equal.

CHAP. III.

ARTILLERY CARRIAGES.

NOMENCLATURE.

The nomenclature and the tables of dimensions and weights given in this chapter, apply to the latest patterns adopted. The parts are enumerated generally in the order in which they are put together.

FIELD GUN CARRIAGES.

There are four gun carriages for field artillery, viz:
One for the 6-pounder gun and the 12-pounder howitzer.
One for the 24-pounder howitzer.
One for the 12-pounder gun and the 32-pounder howitzer.
One for the 12-pounder gun, Napoleon.
The parts of these carriages are all similar, differing only in their dimensions.

Wood.

1 stock, in two pieces; 2 dowels; 2 cheeks; 1 axle body.

Iron.

2 trail handles.
2 bolts and 2 nuts for do.
1 lock chain bolt, 1 washer, and 1 nut.
1 eye plate for lock chain.
1 lock chain, No. 5, 3 rings, 1 toggle.
1 lunette, for the trail.
1 trail plate; 2 rivets.
12 nails, for lunette and trail plate.
1 large pointing ring and plate.
2 bolts and 2 nuts, for do.
1 small pointing ring.
2 bolts and 2 nuts, for do.
2 wheel guard plates.
10 nails, for do.
2 prolonge hooks.

8 nails, for prolonge hooks.
1 stop, for rammer head.
4 nails, for do.
1 ear-plate, for worm.
2 nails, for do.
1 key, for worm.
1 key chain; 1 eye-pin.
1 eye-plate for sponge and rammer chains.
2 screws, for eye-plate.
2 chains and hasps, for sponges and rammers.
2 turnbuckles (*brass*).
2 stud plates, for turnbuckles.
2 trunnion plates.
20 nails, for do., in 6-pdr. and 24-pdr. howitzer carriage.

FIELD GUN CARRIAGES—*Iron*—Continued.

28 nails, in 12-pdr. carriage.
2 chain bolts; 2 bevel washers and 2 nuts.
2 key bolts; 2 nuts.
6 cheek bolts; 4 washers; 6 nuts.
2 cap squares; 2 eye pins.
2 cap square chains; 2 eye pins.
2 cap square keys.
2 key chains; 2 eye pins.
2 D rings, for handspikes.
4 staples, for D rings.
1 linstock-socket.
6 nails, for do.
6 rondelles (*cast iron*).
3 assembling bolts.
3 washers and 3 nuts, for do.
1 washer hook, for lock chain.

2 washer hooks, for handspikes.
1 axletree; the arms, the stop.
2 under straps.
1 axle strap.
1 bevel washer, for 6-pounder axle strap.
3 axle strap bolts; 3 nuts.
2 axle bands.
6 nails, for do.
1 box for elevating screw (*brass*).
2 bolts, for do.; 2 washers; 2 nuts.
1 elevating screw.
2 shoulder washers, } for axletree.
2 linch washers, }
2 linch pins.

2 *wheels*.

LIMBER.

The same limber is used for all field carriages.

Wood.

1 axle body.
2 hounds.
1 fork.
1 splinter bar.

4 foot board brackets.
2 foot boards.
1 pole.
1 pole prop.

Iron.

8 screws, for foot board brackets.
20 nails, for foot boards.
4 rivets and 4 burrs, for hounds.
4 plates, for stay pins; 8 nails.
1 axletree.
1 pintle hook.
3 bolts, for do.; 2 washers; 3 nuts.
1 stay plate, for limber chest.
2 nails, for do.
1 pintle key.
1 key chain; 1 eye pin.
1 tar bucket hook; 2 nails.
2 bolts, for hounds; 2 washers; 2 nuts.
2 under straps.
4 bolts, for under straps; 4 nuts.
2 axle bands; 6 nails.
2 end bands, for splinter bar.
4 rivets, for do.

2 bolts, for hounds and splinter bar.
4 washers and 2 nuts, for do.
1 eye plate, for pole prop socket.
2 middle bands, for splinter bar.
4 trace hooks.
1 fork strap.
2 bolts, for splinter bar and fork.
2 nuts, for do.
1 pole prop socket; 1 rivet.
1 pole prop ferrule: 1 rivet.
1 pole prop chain; 1 toggle.
1 eye pin, for pole prop chain.
1 burr, for eye pin.
2 stay pins, for ammunition chest.
2 keys, for stay pins.
2 key chains; 2 eye pins.
1 rivet and 1 burr, for end of pole.
1 pole bolt; 2 washers; 1 nut.

LIMBER—*Iron*—(Continued.)

1 pole strap and 3 rivets.	2 shoulder washers.
2 pole chains; the links; the ring.	2 linch washers.
1 muff, for pole yoke.	2 linch pins.
1 collar, for muff; in two parts.	
2 branches, for pole yoke; 2 rings.	2 *wheels, No.* 1.
2 bolts, for collar and branches.	1 *ammunition chest.*
1 washer, for muff; 1 key.	

WHEELS.

There are two Nos. of wheels for field carriages. No. 1, for the 6-*pounder gun carriages*, the *caisson*, the *forge*, the *battery wagon*, and for the *limbers* of all field carriages. No. 2, for the 24-*pounder howitzer* and the 12-*pounder gun carriages*. These wheels are of the same form and height, and they fit on the same axletree arm: they differ only in the dimensions of their parts, and consequently in strength and weight.

Wood.	*Iron.*
1 nave.	2 brow bands; 2 end bands.
14 spokes.	12 nails, for bands.
7 fellies.	1 tire.
7 dowels.	7 tire bolts; 7 washers; 7 nuts.
	1 nave box (*cast iron*).

AMMUNITION CHEST.

The same ammunition chest is adapted to the limber and to the caisson.

For the interior arrangements of the chests, for different kinds of ammunition, see chapter on Ammunition.

Wood.

2 sides.	1 frame for cover; 2 sides; 2 ends.
2 ends.	1 panel for cover.
1 principal partition.	1 cover lining.
1 bottom.	

Iron.

34 cut nails, for sides, ends and bottom.
4 screws, for the bottom.
60 copper nails, for cover lining.
4 corner plates, for ends and sides.
2   do.   for ends & bottom.
1   do.   for side & bottom.
96 screws, for corner plates.
1 assembling bolt; 1 nut.
1 turnbuckle (*brass*).
1 washer plate for do.; 2 screws.

1 back stay; 6 screws.
2 front stays; 4 rivets; 8 screws.
2 hinges; 4 rivets; 20 screws.
2 hinge plates; 4 screws.
1 hasp; 1 rivet; 5 screws.
1 hasp plate; 2 screws.
2 handles; 8 rivets.
14 copper washers, for rivets.
56 copper tacks, for washers.
1 cover (*sheet copper*).
216 copper tacks, for cover.

CAISSON.—*Wood.*

1 middle rail.
2 side rails.
1 cross bar.
1 bolster, for front foot board.

1 front foot board.
1 rear foot board.
1 axle body.
1 stock.

Iron.

2 nails, for front foot board.
1 bolt, for do.; 2 washers; 1 nut.
6 nails, for rear foot board.
1 middle assembling bar.
2 bolts, 2 washers and 2 nuts, for do.
1 carriage hook.
1 rear assembling bar.
2 bolts, 2 washers and 2 nuts, for do.
1 bridle, for rear of middle rail.
4 nails, for the bridle.
1 spare wheel axle; the body, 2 ribs, 1 washer, 3 rivets.
1 chain and toggle, for spare wheel axle.
2 stays, for the same; 2 nuts.
1 stay bolt; 1 nut.
1 foot bolt; 1 nut.
1 lock chain bridle.
1 lock chain and toggle.
2 bolts, for lock chain bridle.
2 washers and 2 nuts, for do.
1 lock chain hook; 2 nails.
1 axletree.
2 under straps.
4 bolts, for under straps; 4 nuts.
2 axle bands; 6 nails.
2 rivets for the stock; 2 burrs.
1 lunette; 12 nails.

2 lunette bolts; 2 nuts.
1 key plate, for spare pole.
1 spare pole key.
1 key chain; 1 eye pin.
2 wheel guard plates; 10 nails.
1 stock stirrup.
2 bolts for do.; 2 washers; 2 nuts.
1 axle strap.
1 spare pole ring.
3 bolts, for axle strap; 3 nuts.
8 plates, for stay pins; 16 nails.
4 stay pins.
4 stay pin keys.
4 key chains; 4 eye pins.
1 ring bolt, for spare handspike.
2 washers and 1 nut, for ring bolt.
1 key plate, for handspike; 2 nails.
1 key plate, for shovel; 2 nails.
2 keys, for handspike and shovel.
2 key chains; 2 eye pins.
2 staples, for tool handles.
2 shoulder washers.
2 linch washers.
2 linch pins.

2 *wheels, No. 1.*
2 *ammunition chests.*

TRAVELLING FORGE.

It consists of a *body*, a *bellows house* and *coal box*. For parts, see Ord. Manual, p. 42–43.

To put the bellows in its place.—Remove the coal box from the back of the bellows house; take out the two stay plates at the lower ends of the rabbets in the braces; put the projecting ends of the upper bellows arm in the rabbets, and slide them up until the ends of the lower arm come into their places; put on the stay plates, and fasten them down with the thumb nuts. Screw the brass elbow pipe into its place, through the hole in the sheet iron front of the bellows house; put in the copper pipe, and screw up the collar which connects it with the elbow pipe.

Limber Chest for Travelling Forge and Battery Wagon.

This chest differs from the ammunition chest in the following points, viz:

It has no principal partition, and instead of the assembling bolt, with the washer plate and turnbuckle, it has a *hasp, staple and plate*, fastened by 2 *rivets*.

The *backstay* is fastened by 1 *rivet* and 6 *screws*. The heads of the rivets are not covered with copper washers.

BATTERY WAGON.

The battery wagon carries tools, spare parts of carriages, spare harness, and other stores required for the service of a battery in the field, and for repairs.

Prairie carriage for the 12-*pounder mountain howitzer and mountain rifle.*—For particular parts, see Ord. Manual, 2d ed. p. 47–48.

Prairie ammunition cart.—This is a two-wheeled cart with shafts, carrying four ammunition chests, and one implement chest like those used for the mountain howitzer ammunition. The chests are held in place by stays and a bar fastened with a spring catch behind, so that they may be easily detached. The wheels are like those of the gun carriage, and have the same track. The shafts have hooks at their front ends for the purpose of attaching another horse if necessary, though one horse is sufficient for the ordinary draught.

Gun Carriage for the Mountain Howitzer and Mountain Rifle.

This gun carriage is adapted to transportation on a pack mule; but for occasional draught, when the roads permit, it is furnished with a thill, which is used with the same saddle that carries the pack. For parts, see Ord. Manual, 2d ed. p. 50–51.

Portable forge.—This is used when the capacity of a travelling forge is not required. For parts, see Ord. Manual, p. 51.

SIEGE CARRIAGES.

Gun Carriage.

There are three gun carriages for siege artillery, viz:

One for the 12-pounder gun;
One for the 18-pounder gun;
One for the 24-pounder gun and the 8-inch howitzer.

These carriages are constructed in the same manner, differing only in their dimensions.

When the 8-inch howitzer is mounted on the 24-pounder carriage, a *quoin* is used instead of the elevating screw; the howitzer being too short to rest on the screw.

GARRISON AND SEACOAST CARRIAGES.

The garrison and seacoast carriages are all made of *wrought iron.* They are of four different kinds, viz:

1. The Barbette, front pintle carriage.
2. The Barbette, centre pintle carriage.
3. The casemate carriage.
4. The flank casemate carriage.

Each carriage is composed of a *chassis* and top carriage. The inclination of the *chassis* rails is the same in all the carriages—3°.

PRESERVATION OF CARRIAGES.

Wooden carriages are preserved in well ventilated storehouses protected from the weather, or, in the field, are protected from the sun by a *tarpaulin*. They should have the paint renewed when it is worn off.

Principal dimensions and weights of Field Gun Carriages and Limbers.

DIMENSIONS.	6-pdr. Gun and 12-pdr. Howitzer.	24-pdr. Howitzer.	12-pdr. Gun and 32-pdr. Howitzer.
	In.	In.	In.
Distance between the inside of the trunnion plates,	9.6	11.65	12.15
Diameter of the trunnion holes,	3.7	4.25	4.65
Depth of the centre of trunnion hole below the upper face of the trunnion plate,	1.	0.95	0.95
Distance of axis of trunnions in rear of axis of axletree, the piece being in battery on horizontal ground,	0.5	1.	0.8
Distance from axis of trunnions to axis of axletree,	14.6	16.2	16.6
Height of axis of trunnions above the ground,	43.1	44.8	45.2
Vertical field of fire, above the horizontal line. { Gun,	12°	–	13°
Howitzer;	13°	13°	12°
below the horizontal line. { Gun,	8°	–	7°
Howitzer,	5°	8°	5°
Distance between the points of contact of trail and wheels with the ground line,	74.4	79.8	79.8
Distance from front of wheels to end of trail, the piece being in battery,	116.6	122.75	122.75
Distance of the muzzle of ⎰ Gun, in front of wheels,	5.91	–	15.70
the piece in battery from ⎱ Howitzer, { front of wheels,	–	5.9	12.7
the front of the wheels. { rear of wheels,	1.09		
Length of gun carriage without wheels,	104.4	111.4	113.5
Length of limber without wheels,	161.2	161.2	161.2
Length of limber without wheels or pole,	52.85	52.85	52.85
Length of limber with wheels and pole,	173.08	173.08	173.08
Distance between the centres of the axletrees of gun carriage and limber,	96.	101.7	101.7
Length of the carriage limbered up,	269.08	274.78	274.78
Distance from the muzzle of the piece, { Gun,	279.1	–	294.
when limbered, to the front of pole. { Howitzer,	272.1	283.78	291.
Whole length of the axletree,	78.84	78.84	78.84
Track of the wheels,	60.	60.	60.
Height of wheel,	57.	57.	57.
Dish of finished wheel,	1.5	1.5	1.5
	Lbs.	Lbs.	Lbs.
WEIGHTS. { Gun carriage, without wheels,	540	736	783
Limber, without wheels or ammunition chest,	335	335	335
Ammunition chest, without divisions,	165	165	165
One wheel. { Gun carriage,	180	196	196
{ Limber,	180	180	180
Gun carriage complete, without implements,	900	1128	1175
Limber complete, without implements,	860	860	860
Gun carriage and limber, without implements,	1760	1988	2035

Field and Siege Wagons.

DIMENSIONS AND WEIGHTS.	Caisson.	Forge.	Battery Wagon.	Mortar Wagon.
	In.	In.	In.	In.
Length, - - - - - - -	125 5	130.	154.	143 6
Distance between the axletrees of carriage and limber, - - - - - -	92.	97.8	112.93	102.95
Whole length, when limbered up, - -	274.7	279.	303.13	287.85
Height, above the ground, - -	58.75	70.5	73.55	60.
	Lbs.	Lbs.	Lbs.	Lbs.
WEIGHT. { Carriage body, without wheels, -	432	997	910	984
Limber, without wheels or chest, -	335	335	335	585
One wheel, - - - - -	180.	180	180	404
Carriage and limber, complete, without implements or spare parts, -	1982	2217	2130	3185

CHAP. IV.

ARTILLERY IMPLEMENTS & EQUIPMENTS.

NOMENCLATURE.

Rammer heads are made of ash, maple, or other tough woods. For howitzers they are countersunk to receive the fuzes in ramming shells.

Sponge heads are made one inch less than the diameter of the bore.

Sponges are made of coarse well twisted woolen yarn woven into a warp of strong thread, after the manner of the Brussels carpet. They are also made of sheep-skin, alum dressed, with the wool on.

Sponge covers are made of Russia duck or canvas, painted the same color as the gun carriage.

Ladles are made of sheet copper, and are used for siege, garrison and seacoast guns only.

Handspikes.—The *trail handspike* is made of hickory or young oak, and is used in the service of field carriages. The *manœuvreing handspike* is used with garrison and seacoast carriages. The *shod handspike* is useful in the service of mortars of casemate and barbette carriages. The *truck handspike* and *roller handspike* are made of wrought iron, and used for casemate carriages.

Linstock.—Length of wood 31.5 inches; lower end pointed with iron: used to hold the slow-match when lighted.

Portfire stock.—It has a portfire socket made of brass, with a thumb screw, fastened to a stock of ash 22.5 inches long. It is used to hold the portfire.

Pass box.—Interior dimensions 7 inches square by 14 inches long.

Budge barrel.—20 inches in height, 13 inches in diameter, with a leather hood over top: used in forts for carrying ammunition.

Gunner's haversack, made of leather; 2 sides, 13 inches high, 13 inches wide.

Port fire case, made of sole leather, to contain 12 port fires.

Tube pouch, made of leather; the sides 4.25 inches high, 7.25 inches long. The priming wire and gunner's gimlet are carried with the tube pouch in the loops.

Priming wire: iron wire 0.75 inch diameter, formed with a ring 2 inches diameter at the head, and pointed; length of stem, for siege and garrison guns, 14 inches; length for field guns, 8 inches.

Gunner's gimlet, like the priming wire, terminating in a gimlet point.

Vent punch: the *body* (steel wire) 0.175 inch diameter, 4.3 inches long.

Thumbstall (buckskin): *cushion*, stuffed with hair, 2.5 inches long, 1 inch thick.

Port fire cutter: blades (steel) 2.37 inches long, with a notch 1 inch long and 0.4 inch deep in one of them, 1 inch from the joint—*handles* with bows 2 inches by 1 inch—whole length 7 inches.

Tangent scale (sheet brass, No. 13): *flange* 0.5 inch wide, cut to fit the base ring of the piece; upper edge cut into notches for each ¼ degree elevation.

Table of Tangent Scales for Field Guns and Howitzers.

ELEVATION.	GUNS.		HOWITZERS.		
	6-pdr.	12-pdr.	12-pdr.	24-pdr.	32-pdr.
	Inches.	Inches.	Inches.	Inches.	Inches.
1° 15′	0.256	0.333	0.252	0.289	0.331
2°	1.025	1.334	0.945	1.138	1.310
3°	2.051	2.670	1.870	2.271	2.618
4°	3.077	4.006	2.791	3.400	3.920

Pendulum hausse, or tangent scale.

The *scale* is made of sheet brass, No. 13. At the lower end is a brass bulb, filled with lead. The *slider* is of thin brass, and is retained in any desired position on the scale by means of a brass set screw with a milled head. The scale is passed through a slit in a piece of steel, with which it is connected by a brass screw, forming a pivot on which the scale can vibrate laterally; this slit is made long enough to allow the scale to take a vertical position in any ordinary cases of inequality of the ground on which the wheels of the carriage may stand. The ends of this piece of steel form two journals, by means of which the scale is supported on the seat attached to the gun, and is at liberty to vibrate in the direction of the axis of the piece.

The *seat* is of iron, and is fastened to the base of the breech by 3 *screws*, in such a manner that the centres of the two journal notches shall be at a distance from the axis equal to the radius of the base ring.

A *muzzle sight*, of iron, is screwed into the swell of the muzzle of guns, or into the middle of the muzzle ring of howitzers. The height of this sight is equal to the dispart of the piece, so that a line from the top of the muzzle sight to the pivot of the tangent scale is parallel to the axis of the piece; consequently, the vertical plane of sight passing through the centre line of the scale and the top of the muzzle sight, will be also parallel to the axis, in any position of the piece; the tangent scale will, therefore, always indicate correctly the angle which the plane of sight makes with the axis.

The seat for suspending the hausse on the gun is adapted in each piece, according to the varying inclination of the base of the breech to the axis. The hausse, the seat and the muzzle sight, are marked for the kind of gun to which they belong. The hausse, when not in use, is carried in a leather pouch suspended to a shoulder strap.

The graduations on the scale are the tangents of each quarter of a degree, to a radius equal to the distance between the muzzle sight and the centre of the journal notches, which are, in all cases, one inch in rear of the base ring.

In some rifled cannon the sight is placed on the *trunnion* instead of the *muzzle*. The *breech sight* is then placed on the side, so that the line of the sights is in a vertical plane parallel to the axis of the bore. In *all rifled cannon* the projectile deviates in the direction in which it revolves, to the right. This deviation is to be obviated in practice, by pointing to the left of the object.

Tangent Scales for Pendulum Hausses for Field Guns and Howitzers.

	FOR GUNS.		FOR HOWITZERS.			
	6-pdr.	12-pdr.	12-pdr.	24-pdr.	32-pdr.	
	In.	In.	In.	In.	In.	
Radius of base ring,	5.15	6.5	5.0	6.0	6.9	
Dispart, -	1.025	1.33	0.9	1.125	1.3	Height of muzzle sight.
Tang. 1°	1.042	1.349	0.931	1.128	1.310	
2°	2.084	2.698	1.862	2.275	2.621	
3°	3.124	4.046	2.792	3.412	3.933	
4°	4.164	5.392	3.722	4.548	5.248	
5°	5.203	6.737	4.650	5.683	6.566	

Gunner's level.—This is made of sheet brass; the lower part is cut in the form of a crescent, the points of which are made of steel; a small spirit level is fastened to one side of the plate, parallel to the line joining the points of the crescent, and a slider is fastened to the same side of the plate, perpendicular to the axis of the level. The instrument is useful in marking the points of sight on siege guns and mortars when the platform is not perfectly level.

Vent cover, for field pieces (leather); 6 inches long, 4 inches wide, with a *copper pin* riveted to it. The length of the strap varies with the size of the piece. In permanent batteries sheet lead may be used for vent covers.

Fuze setter (brass); the *handle*, upper end slightly rounded, the *cup* 2.1 inches diameter; depth, 0.3 inch. Whole length, 5 to 6 inches.

Fuze mallet (dogwood or oak), in one piece; *head*, 5.5 inches long, 4 inches diameter; *handle,* 7.5 inches long, 1.25 inch diameter.

Fuze saw (tenon saw); 10 inch blade.

Fuze rasp; 12 inch wood rasp.

Fuze auger, for boring out the composition to any required depth. *Bit* 0.2 inch diameter, sliding in a brass *socket* graduated to 10ths of an inch, and held by a thumb screw in the side; *handle,* of hard wood.

Fuze gimlet; common gimlet, 0.2 : used for boring across the composition instead of sawing off the fuze.

Shell plug screw (iron); *stem* 3 inches long, cut with a deep, sharp thread; *eye* 2 inches in diameter.

Fuze plug reamer.—A conical steel reamer, for reaming the holes for paper fuzes in the wooden fuze plugs.

Fuze extractor.—The *inner screw* and its *stem* are made of steel, and riveted into the *handle,* which is of iron. It is used for extracting fuzes.

Gunner's pincers.—Made of iron, with steel jaws 1 inch wide; whole length 10.5 inches.

Gunner's callipers.—Made of sheet brass, with steel points. The graduations show the diameters of guns and of shot, linear inches, degrees of the circle, etc.

Gunner's quadrant (wood); a graduated *quadrant* of 6 inches radius attached to a rule 23.5 inches long. It has a *plumb line* and *bob,* which are carried, when not in use, in a hole in the end of the rule, covered by a brass plate.

Maul, for driving pickets; *head* (elm or hickory) 6 inches diameter, 8 inches long; *handle* (ash) 1½ inch diameter, 24 inches long, with an iron band on each end, 1 inch wide, ¼ inch thick.

Pointing wire, for mortars (iron wire No. 7); 20 inches long.

Quoin, for siege mortars (oak); length, 19.5 inches; height, 7.85 inches; *handle,* 6 inches long.

Chock, for casemate carriage; small wedge, with a handle on one side.

Plummet, for mortars; *line* and *bob.*

Scraper, for do. (iron); *handle* 0.5 inch by 0.3 inch square, 27 inches long; one end formed like a *spoon;* the other, a *scraper.*

Spatula, for mortars (ash or hickory); *handle*, 16.5 inches long; *blade*, 6 inches; *square end*, 3 inches long.

Splints (white pine); 6 inches long; 0.25 inch thick at the large end; 1 inch wide.

Wiper, for the chambers of mortars; tow cloth, 1 yard square.

Gunner's sleeve, for mortars (serge or flannel).

Basket, for mortar implements: of strong wicker work, 18 inches in diameter, 12 inches deep.

Tarpaulins are made of two sizes: large, 15 by 12 feet; small, 5 feet square.

Tompions, for 8-inch siege howitzers and mortars, and 10-inch mortar.

Broom, for mortar batteries (hickory or birch).

Shell hooks (iron); 2 *branches*, 0.5 inch diameter, in shape of an *S*, joined by a *rivet*. Used for lifting large shells.

Tow hook (iron); *handle*, 0.4 inch diameter, 13 inches long; *hook*, 1 inch; the other end forms a *hammer*, 0.6 inch diameter, 2 inches long. Used for unpacking limber chest.

Funnel, for filling shells (copper or tin): diameter of *funnel*, 3.3 inches; diameter of *pipe*, 0.7 inch; length of pipe, 2 inches.

Powder measures.—They are made of sheet copper, from No. 16 to No. 20. The bottom is made with a flange .1 inch deep, turned downwards, and it is brazed or soldered to the sides.

Prolonge.—3.5 inch hemp rope of 4 strands; on one end a *toggle*, and 3 *round links* in a *thimble*; on the other end a *hook* and a *thimble*.

Sponge bucket for field gun carriages, made of sheet iron. Diameter 7.8 inches; height 9 inches.

Tar bucket, made of sheet iron. Diameter 7.2 inches; height 8 inches.

Water bucket, for travelling forge, made of oak. Diameter at top 11 inches; bottom 10.25 inches; height 11 inches.

Watering bucket for field service, made of sole leather, bottom of two thicknesses. Interior diameter of bucket at top 12 inches; at bottom 10 inches; height 9 inches.

Interior dimensions of Cylindrical Powder Measures.

Contents.		Diameter and height.	Contents.		Diameter and height.
Lbs.	oz.	In.	Lbs.	oz.	In.
0	1	1.337	2	0	4.240
0	2	1.685	2	8	4.571
0	4	2.122	3	0	4.857
0	8	2.673	4	0	5.346
1	0	3 368	4	8	5.560
1	4	3.628	6	0	6.120
1	8	3.855	8	0	6.736

Shovel.—*Blade*, sheet iron, pointed with steel.

Pick axe.—Iron, pointed at both ends with steel.

Felling axe.—*Blade*, with steel edge, and *hickory* handle, 27 inches long.

Hand bill, or *Bill hook.*—Iron, with steel edges. Whole length *blade*, 8.25 inches; hook 1 inch long; handle (hickory), 7.5 inches long.

Drag rope.—4 inch rope, 28 feet long, with a *thimble* worked in a loop at one end, and a thimble and hook at the other end— 6 *handles*, wood, 12 inches long, 1.5 inch diameter, fastened to the rope at the distance of 4 feet apart, and at the same distance from the ends of the rope.

Men's harness.—4 inch rope, 18 feet long, with *thimbles* and a *hook*. Instead of handles, *loops* made of leather are used, and fastened to the rope in pairs.

Screw jack, for field service. Height of stand 19 inches; length of screw 15 inches.

Weights of Implements and Equipments.

KIND.		Weight.	KIND.		Weight.
		Lbs.			Lbs.
Woolen sponges,	42-pdr. -	0.7	Fuze plug reamer, - -		0.3
	32-pdr. -	0.65	Fuze extractor, - -		3.53
	24-pdr. -	0.5	Gunner's pincers, - -		0.85
	18-pdr. -	0 4	Gunner's callipers, - -		0.5
	12-pdr. -	0.35	Gunner's quadrant, wood, -		0.84
	6-pdr. -	0.25	Gunner's perpendicular, -		0.6
Sponge covers,	42-pdr.	0.28	Maul, - - - -		10.
	6-pdr.	0.14	Pointing wire, - - -		0.08
Trail handspikes, - -		7.25	Quoin, for siege mortars, -		7.
Manœuvreing handspike, -		8.28	Chock, - - - -		1.4
Shod handspike and long ma-			Plummet, - - -		1.
nœuvreing handspike, -		12.	Scraper, - - -		2.3
Truck handspike, - -		18.5	Spatula, - - -		0.75
Roller handspike, - -		7.	Splint, - - - -		0.03
Linstock, - - -		0.9	Gunner's sleeve, - -		0.25
Port-fire stock, - - -		0.65	Basket, - - - -		4.
Pass box, - - -		7.	Tarpaulins,	Small, -	9.
Budge barrel, - - -		15.5		Large, -	54.
Gunner's haversack, -		1.86	Mortar tompions,	8-inch, -	5.
Port-fire case, - -		1.55		10-inch, -	7.
Tube pouch, - - -		0.95	Broom (hickory), -		3.75
Priming horn, - - -		0.86	Shell hooks, - -		2.
Priming wire, - - -		0.08	Tow hooks, - - -		0.6
Gunner's gimlet, - -		0.08	Funnel, - - -		0.32
Vent pouch, - - -		0.08	Powder measures.	4 oz. -	0.3
Thumbstall, - - -		0.003		8 oz. -	0.5
Port-fire cutter, - -		0.77		1 lb. -	0.75
Tangent scale, - - -		0.21		3 lbs. -	1.6
Pendulum hausse and case, -		0.65	Prolonge, - - -		18.
Cannon lock, - - -		2.75	Sponge bucket, -		10.
Lock cover, - - -		0.9	Tar bucket, - -		7.
Vent cover, - - -		0.45	Water bucket, wood, -		10.
Lanyard for friction primers, -		0.10	Watering bucket, leather, -		8.
Fuze setter, - - -		2.66	Shovel, - - -		4.75
Fuze mallet, - - -		2.75	Pickaxe, - - -		6.5
Fuze saw, - - -		0.75	Felling axe, - -		6.
Fuze rasp, - - -		0.75	Hand bill, - - -		2.
Fuze auger, - - -		0.3	Drag rope, - - -		16.5
Fuze gimlet, - - -		0.1	Men's harness, - -		23.
Shell plug screw, - -		0.31	Screw jack, - -		25.

CHAP. V.

ARTILLERY HARNESS.

The construction of the field carriages requires a harness different, in some respects, from that of common wagons. The limber having no sweep bar, the pole is supported directly by the wheel horses, by means of a chain which connects the hames with the pole yoke of the limber; and, in order to diminish the weight at the end of the pole, the leading bars are dispensed with, the traces of the leaders being attached to those of the wheel horses.

The same harness is perfectly adapted, also, to the siege carriages; but as these are arranged for draught in the ordinary manner, common wagon harness may be used with them if necessary.

Black leather is used for the harness when not otherwise specified. It should be of the best quality, and the strongest leather is selected for the parts which are exposed to the greatest strain, such as traces and breeching.

Head gear.—The *head gear* is made of strong black bridle leather, not less than .1 inch thick. It consists of the *halter*, the *bridle* and the *bit*.

The *bit* is made of *iron, japanned.* The *curb chain* consists of 19 links.

Driver's saddle.—The frame is made of beech, and covered with *canvas* or *raw hide.*

Valise saddle.—The frame like the *driver's saddle*, only smaller.

Valise—made of black bridle leather, lined with cotton ticking.

Whip.—The stock is of hickory or raw hide, about 30 inches long.

Leg guard.—The body is made of stout kip leather, with a plate of iron 0.1 inch thick fastened to it.

Nose bag.—The bottom is made of stiff leather, 6 inches diameter and 4 inches deep, to which a bag of strong linen is sewed.

Draught harness.—It consists of the *collar*, the *hames*, the *traces*, the *crupper*.

Breeching includes the *breech strap*, the *hip strap*, the *breast strap*, the *pole strap*. The *breast strap* and *pole strap* are made of three layers of thick harness leather.

Pole pad is placed on the end of the pole to prevent the lead horses from being injured.

PACK-SADDLE AND HARNESS FOR MOUNTAIN ARTILLERY.

The mountain howitzer and its carriage are either carried on pack-mules, or the gun is mounted on the carriage and drawn by mules harnessed to it.

The ammunition, forage and tool chests are carried on pack-mules; or, when the roads are good, may be carried in common carts.

The equipment is the same whether the gun and carriage are packed or drawn, except that the lashing-girth and lashing-rope are not required for draught.

Composition.—The harness complete is composed of the *head gear*, the *pack saddle*—which is common for packing the gun carriage or chests—the *crupper*, the *breeching*, the *breast strap*, and the *lashing girth* and *rope*.

Packing the Mountain Howitzer.

The howitzer is placed on the pack saddle, the muzzle to the front, in the recesses cut in the bows and transoms: it is lashed with the lashing rope. The shafts are placed upside down on the same pack saddle, the cross bar on the neck of the cascable: the shafts are lashed with the bow straps.

The carriage is placed on the pack saddle, the axletree against the front face of the front bow: it is fastened by the lashing rope. The wheels are placed on the same pack with the carriage, one on each side, the small end of the nave against the pack between the bows, one of the spokes resting on the arm of the axletree; they are lashed with the bow straps.

The ammunition chests are suspended with chains, on hooks, on each side of the pack, and lashed with lashing ropes.

To place the Howitzer on the Saddle.

Three men load the howitzer on the mule. Introduce the rammer head into the bore; place the loop of the handspike over the cascable; carry the piece to the saddle, approaching by the croup; raise it and place it in its bed. Three men load the carriage, taking hold of it by the arms of the axletree and by the end of the trail.

Four men load two ammunition chests and hook the 4 chains at the same time. The load ought to be fastened securely, so as to form as it were a part of the animal, and should be raised as little as possible above the mule's back.

HORSE EQUIPMENTS FOR THE CAVALRY SERVICE.

A complete set of horse equipments for cavalry troops consists of 1 *bridle*, 1 *watering bridle*, 1 *halter*, 1 *saddle*, 1 *pair of saddle bags*, 1 *saddle blanket*, 1 *surcingle*, 1 *pair of spurs*, 1 *curry comb*, 1 *horse brush*, 1 *picket pin*, and 1 *lariat* (1 *link* and 1 *nose bag*, when specially required).

The saddle adopted in the C. S. service is known as Jenifer's saddle.

GENERAL DIRECTIONS FOR SHOEING HORSES.

The shoe should be forged to fit the form of the foot: it should project on the outside at the end of the heel about its thickness, beginning at the last hole; should be flush with the hoof at the toe and on the inside; the heels generally short and thin. The holes in the outer quarter should be farther from the edge, and in the inner quarter nearer the edge; in the front shoe nearer the toe, and in the hind shoe nearer the heel. Make the lower face of the shoe perfectly flat, and try it on an iron table. The shoe should bear equally all around on the wall of the foot, and not at all on the sole.

A judicious preparation of the foot for the shoe is of the greatest importance, strict attention being paid to its peculiarities.

Shoes should not be allowed to remain on more than five weeks, when they should be removed, the useless hoof paired off, and the shoe replaced if it still be good. This should be regulated by the length of the hoof rather than by the wear of the shoe. Rough shoeing differs from ordinary shoeing only in the form of the nails, the heads being longer and more pointed.

Harness required for each Horse.

	Saddle-horse.	WHEELERS.		LEADERS.		Weight.
		Near side.	Off side.	Near side.	Off side.	
						Lbs.
Halter,	1	1	1	1	1	3.0
Bridle,	1	1	1	1	1	3.0
Coupling-strap,	–	–	1	–	1	0.5
Driver's saddle,	1	–	–	–	–	16.25
Valise-saddle,	–	1	–	1	–	7.78
Valise,	–	–	1	–	1	4.5
Collar and collar-strap,	–	1	1	1	1	4.25
Hames and strap and 2 turning-straps,	–	1	1	1	1	9.25
Pair of traces, { Wheel,	–	1	1	–	–	9.75
{ Leading,	–	–	–	1	1	11.75
Trace-loops and belly-band,	–	1	1	1	1	1.
Loin-straps and trace-loops, { Wheel,	–	1	1	–	–	0.75
{ Leading,	–	–	–	1	1	0.875
Crupper,	–	1	1	1	1	0.75
Breeching and hip-strap,	–	1	1	–	–	3.6
Breast-strap,	–	1	–	–	–	4.75
Leg-guard,	–	1	–	1	–	2.
Whip,	–	1	–	1	–	0.35
Nose-bag,	–	1	1	1	1	1.12
Pole-strap (on the carriage-pole),	–	1	1	1	1	2.
Pole-pad, " "	–	–	–	–	–	1.5
		Lbs.	Lbs.	Lbs.	Lbs.	
Weight. { For each horse,	–	59 82	54.9	51.60	47.77	
{ Set for 2 horses,	–	113.82		99.37		

Preservation of Harness in Store.

The store houses should be well ventilated, not too dry, but free from dampness. The different articles should be arranged according to kind and class, separated or in bundles according to their nature, so placed as to touch each other and the walls as little as possible, having a free circulation of air about them—*saddles* on trestles or bars—*collars* hung on pins—*hames*, with their straps, and *traces* with chains and hooks, hung up; the traces hanging vertically—*side straps* and *bellybands* piled on the floor or on shelves—*surcingles* and *breast straps* stretched on racks—*halters*, *bridles*, *reins*, etc., hung up in bundles of five or ten—*hames straps*, *collar straps*, etc., hung up in bundles of ten or twenty—*bits*, *curb chains*, *trace hooks*, in boxes.

All these articles should be examined and cleaned at least four times a year.

The leather articles are brushed and greased with *neat's foot oil*, as often as their condition requires: if they have a reddish hue, mix a little lamp black with the oil. First brush the leather carefully, then pass over it a sponge wet with lukewarm water; grease it slightly on the hair side, applying the oil with a soft brush before the leather is quite dry. In general, new leather is not greased until it has been in store three years, unless it should be found to require it. Iron parts which are not japanned or tinned, or from which the coating is rubbed off, are greased with tallow.

CHAP. VI.

SMALL ARMS, SWORDS, SABRES, &c.

HISTORY OF SMALL ARMS AND PROJECTILES.

Portable fire arms were invented about the middle of the 14th century. They consisted of a tube of iron fired from a support, and weighed about 75 pounds.

Arquebuse.—The difficulty of firing "hand cannon," arising from their weight, was overcome by making them shorter, and supporting them on a tripod by means of trunnions. They were called *arquebuses*, and fired with a match by the hand.

Pistol.—The first pistol was a wheel lock *arquebuse*, invented 1545, in Pistoia, a city of Tuscany; hence its name.

Musket.—The musket was first used by the Spaniards, under Charles V. The balls weighed 2 ounces, and the piece had to be supported on a forked stick. The calibre was afterwards reduced; and hence the present smooth bored musket.

Match lock.—To avoid disturbing the aim, a lock was devised, which consisted of a lever holding at its extremity a lighted match. The lever was pressed down with the finger until the end of the match touched the priming.

Wheel lock, invented 1517, consisted of a grooved wheel of steel, made to act on a piece of alloy of iron and antimony, placed near the priming charge of powder.

Flint lock, derived from the wheel lock by substituting flint and a steel battery for the wheel and the alloy, was generally introduced in the French army in 1680.

Percussion lock was introduced in 1842, and now all arms are made with this lock. The percussion cap was invented in the United States in 1817.

Bayonet.—Before the invention of the bayonet fire arms were combined with pikes in such a manner that one afforded protection to the other. It was first made at *Bayonne* 1640; hence its name. It was formed of a steel blade attached to a handle of wood, which was inserted into the bore of the barrel when used. Afterwards the wooden handle was replaced by a hollow socket, thus rendering the musket a pike as well as a fire arm, changing the formation of infantry from six ranks to three and two.

Rifle.—The *rifle* first made its appearance at Leipsic 1498. The grooves were parallel to the axis of the bore, for the purpose of diminishing friction. It was accidentally discovered that *spiral* grooves gave greater accuracy to the projectile. About 1600 it was somewhat used as a military arm for firing spherical balls.

Accuracy of the rifle.—In 1742 Robins pointed out the superiority of the elongated form of projectile, and demonstrated that the irregular deviations of the projectile fired from a smooth bored musket, were due to the revolution of the ball around an axis not coincident with the axis of the bore; thus producing by the resistance of the air an unequal pressure on the sides of the ball. This irregular revolution is due to the eccentricity of the centre of gravity of the ball, and the position which the centre of gravity occupies in reference to the axis of the bore, together with the lodgments of the ball near the muzzle. When by the grooves of the rifle the projectile is made to revolve on an axis coincident with the axis of the bore, there is no inequality in the *resistance of the air* on the sides of the projectile, and hence no pressure to cause a deviation from the normal trajectory.

Range of the rifle.—The *superior range* of the rifle over the smooth bored musket, is due entirely to the fact that in the rifle, windage is entirely cut off by forcing the ball into the grooves, and by the shape of the projectile the resistance of the air is diminished; thus the explosive force is greater and the resistance less.

Forcing.—"Forcing" is the operation by which the projectile is made to take hold of the grooves of a *rifled barrel*, and follow them in its passage through the bore. At first this was effected by driving the projectile down with a mallet applied to the point of the ramrod, and then by wrapping the projectile in a *patch* of cloth, greased. Owing to this slow and difficult method of load-

ing, the rifle was not introduced as a military arm until quite a
recent period, when this difficulty was overcome.

Delvigne.—In 1827 M. Delvigne, an officer of the French infantry, introduced the following method of "forcing:" At the
bottom of the breech was a small chamber to contain the powder.
The ball, when resting on the shoulders of the chamber, was
forced into the grooves by two or three blows with the ramrod.
This method was soon abandoned, as the ball was much disfigured.

Thouvenin.—*Col. Thouvenin* replaced the chamber of *Del-*
vigne by a spindle of iron screwed into the centre of the breech
screw. The base of the elongated bullet resting on the point of
the spindle, was *forced* into the grooves by two or three blows of
the ramrod. This was the celebrated *carabine à tige*, or *stem*
rifle, and is the first military arm in which an *elongated* projectile
was used.

Greener.—The first attempt to force a projectile by the action
of powder was made in 1836 by Mr. Greener of London. He
inserted a conical pewter wedge in the base of an oblong bullet,
which was driven in by the force of powder so as to force the exterior of the bullet into the grooves of the rifle.

Minié.—Some years after this, Col. Minié proposed a projectile
on the same principle. But instead of a solid wedge, he inserted
in the conical cavity at the base of the bullet, a cup of sheet iron.

Present method.—Shortly after the introduction of the *Minié*
bullet, it was discovered, simultaneously, in this country and in
England, that by giving a suitable size and shape to the cavity in
the projectile, the expansive power of the gas alone, without the
wedge or *culot*, was sufficient to force the projectile into the
grooves.

The C. S. bullet is a cylinder surmounted by a conoid, weighs
550 grains, and has three grooves around the bore to hold the
grease for lubricating, and to guide the bullet in its flight, preserving its point foremost.

The English bullet (known as the Pritchett bullet) has a perfectly smooth exterior. A conical wedge of box wood is inserted

in the cavity of the bore, chiefly to preserve its form in being transported.

Charge of powder.—The charge of the old smooth bored musket was from one-half to one-third the weight of the projectile. The charge for elongated expanding bullets varies from one-tenth to one-seventh the weight of the projectile.

DIFFERENT KINDS OF SMALL ARMS.

The small arms adopted for service are:
The rifle musket, model 1855.
The rifle musket, model 1842.
The rifle, model 1855.
The rifle, model 1842, reamed out to .577 inch.

No model has yet been adopted for a carbine for the cavalry service; several different patterns are now in the hands of the troops.

A *repeating pistol* is issued to the cavalry.

The uniform calibre of .577 inch is adopted in the C. S. service for all *rifles* and *rifle muskets*.

Rifle musket.—The rifle musket of model 1855 combines in one piece the range and accuracy of the rifle, with the advantages of the smooth bored musket, as regards lightness, quickness of loading, and facility of handling, as a pike.

Length of barrel,	40 inches.
Length of arm with bayonet,	74 "
Weight of barrel,	4.25 lbs.
Weight of arm complete,	9.90 "
Weight of projectile,	550 grs.
Weight of powder,	60 "
Initial velocity,	960 feet.

Rifle.—The rifle differs from the rifle musket, in having a shorter and stouter barrel, a sword bayonet and brass mountings.

Length of barrel,	33 inches.
Length of arm with bayonet,	72 "
Weight of barrel,	4.80 lbs.

Weight of arm complete, - - 13. lbs.

Charge (projectile and powder) same as rifle musket.

Initial velocity, - - 910 feet.

Enfield rifle.—Many are in the C. S. service, obtained by purchase and capture—so called because made after the model of the English government rifle, manufactured at Enfield. It has three grooves.

Calibre, - - - - .577 inches.
Length of barrel, - - - 39. "
Length of arm with bayonet, - 73. "
Weight of arm complete, - - 9.19 lbs.
Weight of projectile, ⎱ as rifle musket.
Weight of powder, ⎰ " "
Twist, - - one turn in 6 feet 6 inches.

Smooth bored musket.—The calibre of the *smooth bored musket* (model 1822 and 1840) is considerably larger than the rifle musket; the former being .69 inch, and the latter .577 inch, and with it, more powder is required to project a ball of less weight, than with the rifle. Many of these models (1822 and 1840) are in our service, some of them being still used with the flint lock.

Length of barrel, - - - 42. inches.
Length with bayonet (model 1822), - 73.6 "
" " " (model 1840), - 75.8 "
Weight of arm complete (model 1840), 10.18 lbs.
Weight of round ball, - - 463 grains.
Weight of powder, - - - 110 "

English smooth bored musket.—Some smooth bored muskets of English manufacture (old models) are in our service of very large calibre, being .75 inch. Special ammunition is made for them.

Musketoon.—The *musketoon* is a short musket, having barrel 26 inches in length and calibre .69 inch. This is an old model, and was formerly issued to the cavalry and artillery in the U. S. service. Some are now used by the C. S. cavalry.

Belgian rifle.—The Belgian rifle is a *carbine à tige*, having a *stem* in the chamber of the breech, with a calibre of .70 inch. It has *four* grooves, and is properly used with a solid projectile of 756 grains in weight.

Brunswick rifle.—This rifle has *two grooves*, which diminish in depth to a certain distance in the barrel, when they are eased off smooth with the bore—calibre about .70 inch. Some of the Belgian and Brunswick rifles are in the C S. service, both by purchase and capture.

Carbine.—The term *carbine* is applied to an arm used by mounted troops, intermediate in weight and length between the rifle and pistol. The name is derived from a company of cavalry called *carabins*, to whom they were first issued. There are several different varieties in our service.

Breech loading carbines.—Nearly all the carbines in our service are *breech loading*. All may be divided in two classes, those which have *movable* chambers and those which have *fixed* chambers. The following kinds are in our service :

Hall's carbine.—This is an old carbine with movable chamber, calibre .52 inch, length of barrel 21 inches. It was formerly used with a flint lock in the U. S. service. Some with percussion locks are in the C. S. service.

Burnside's carbine has a calibre of .54 inch, and a movable chamber. The cartridge is enclosed in a conical brass case.

Sharp's carbine has a fixed chamber. That in our service has a calibre of .52 inch.

Maynard's carbine has a fixed chamber. There are two calibres in our service. Large size, calibre .52 inch. Small size, calibre .36 inch. *Maynard's primer*, attached to this carbine, contains 60 primers in a row, on a tape or ribbon of paper. A primer is moved under the hammer by the act of cocking. The charge is enclosed in a cylinder of sheet brass.

Merrill's carbine has a fixed chamber, and calibre .54 inch.

Colt's revolving carbine has a cylinder with *six* chambers, and a rifled barrel, of calibre .56 inch.

Colt's pistol is used in our service, and is constructed on the revolving principle, with a cylinder containing *six* chambers, and a rifled barrel.

There are two kinds in use ; *Colt's army pistol* has a barrel inches in length, of .44 inch calibre. The *navy pistol* has a barrel inches in length, of .33 inch calibre.

Grape-shot pistol.—This pistol is manufactured by M. Le Mat of Paris. It has a *cylinder* which revolves, containing *nine* chambers, a *rifled barrel* and a *smooth-bored barrel.* The latter receives a charge of eleven buckshot, and is fired by a slight change in the hammer. Some are in our service.

NOMENCLATURE.

The parts of a *musket* or *rifle,* are the *band, breech screw, tang screw, cone bayonet, lock, two side screws, mountings, ramrod, stock* and *tip.*

Lock.—The parts of the *lock,* are *lock plate, hammer, tumbler, bridle, bridle screw, sear, sear spring, sear-spring screw, main spring, swivel, tumbler-and-swivel pin.*

Mountings.—The mountings consist of *upper and lower bands, middle band, middle-band swivel, band springs, side-screw washers, guard, guard plate, guard bow, trigger, trigger screw, butt plate, two screws for butt plate.*

Implements.—The implements for use in the field, are *screw driver,* with *cone wrench, wiper, ball screw* and *spring vice.*

Principal Dimensions, Weights, etc. of Small Arms.

		RIFLE MUSKETS.		RIFLES.	
		1855.	1842.	1855.	1842.
DIMENSIONS.		Inches.	Inches.	Inches.	Inches.
BARREL.	Diameter of bore, - -	0.577	0 69	0.577	0.577
	Variation allowed, more, -	0.0025	0.015	0.0025	0.0025
	Diameter at muzzle, -	0.78	0.85	0.90	0.90
	Diameter at breech between flats, - - -	1.14	1.25	1.14	1.15
	Length without breech-screw,	40.	42.	33.	33.
BAYONET—Length of blade, -		18.	18.	21.7	21.7
RAMROD—Length, - - -		39.60	41.70	33.00	33.00
STOCK, with butt-plate and tip—Length,		52.85			
ARM COMPLETE.	Length without bayonet, -	55.85	57.80	49.3	48.8
	With bayonet fixed, -	73.85	75.80	71.8	71.3
	With butt-piece, -				
GROOVES.	Number, - -	3.	3.	3.	3.
	Twist, uniform, 1 turn in -	6 ft.	6 ft.	6 ft.	6 ft.
	Width, - - -	0.30	0.36	0.30	0.30
	Depth at muzzle, - -	.005	.005	.005	.005
	Depth at breech, - -	.015	.015	.013	.013
WEIGHTS.		Lbs.	Lbs.	Lbs.	Lbs.
BARREL, without breech-screw, -		4.28	4.19	4.8	4.8
LOCK, with side-screws, -		.81	.95	.81	.55
BAYONET, - - -		.72	0.64	2.15	2.15
BUTT-PLATE, - -		.375			
ARM COMPLETE.	Without bayonet, -	9.18	9.51	9.93	9.68
	With bayonet, -	9.90	10.15	12.08	11.83
	With butt-piece, -				

What is commonly known as the *Mississippi rifle* in the C. S. service, was made after the model of 1842, with a calibre of .54.

AMMUNITION FOR SMALL ARMS.

Bullets for the military service are made by pressure. One press is capable of making 3,000 bullets in an hour. Some are also cast in moulds, and afterwards *swaged* in a die to the proper size and shape.

Cartridges.—The cartridge is composed of the *bullet* and the *cylinder* which contains the powder. The cylinder is now attached to the bullet without a wrapper or twine, by being compressed in an incision, by machinery, in its base.

Pistol cartridges.—The powder cylinder of Colt's cartridge is made of combustible paper (prepared after the manner of gun cotton); it is attached to the base of the ball by gum, and is inserted in the piece entire.

Percussion caps.—The cap for small arms is made of copper; it is very slightly conical, with a rim at the open end for convenience in handling. The caps are formed by a machine which cuts a star or *blank* from the sheet and transfers it to a die in which the cap is shaped by means of a punch. For use in Boughton's machine, the copper is first cut into strips, from which the blanks are cut and the caps formed; Wright's machine cuts the blanks from the whole sheet and forms the cap. The first machine makes 2,196 caps, the second, 2,314 caps, from a sheet of the size above mentioned. Each machine can make about 5,000 caps an hour.

The powder with which the caps are charged, consists of *fulminate of mercury*, mixed with half its weight of saltpetre. Each cap contains *half a grain* of percussion powder, which is protected from moisture by a drop of varnish.

PRESERVATION OF ARMS IN SERVICE.

The officers, non-commissioned officers and soldiers should be instructed and practiced in the nomenclature of the arms, the manner of dismounting and mounting them, and the precautions and care required for their preservation.

Each soldier should have a screw driver and a wiper, and each squad of ten a band spring and tumbler punch, and a spring vice. No other implements should be used in taking arms apart or in setting them up.

In the inspection of arms, officers should attend to the qualities essential to service, rather than to a bright polish on the exterior of the arms. The arms should be inspected in the quarters at least once a month, with the barrel and lock separated from the stock.

Taking arms to Pieces.

To take apart the rifle musket, model 1855:

1. Unfix the bayonet.
2. Put the tompion in the muzzle of the barrel.
3. Draw the ramrod.
4. Turn the tang screw.
5. Take off the lock: to do this, first put the hammer at half-cock, then unscrew partially the side screws, and, with a slight tap on the head of each screw with a wooden instrument, loosen the lock from its bed in the stock; then turn out the side screws, and remove the lock with the left hand.
6. Remove the side screws, taking care not to disturb the washers.
7. Take off the upper band.
8. Take off the middle band.
9. Take off the lower band.
10. Take out the barrel.

In doing this, turn the musket horizontally, with the barrel downward, holding the barrel loosely with the left hand below the rear sight, the right hand grasping the stock by the handle; and if it does not leave the stock, tap the tompion in the muzzle gently against the ground or floor, which will loosen the breech end from the stock. This is preferable to lifting the barrel out by the muzzle, because if the tang of the breech-screw should bind in the wood, the head of the stock would be liable to be split by raising the muzzle first.

The foregoing parts of the rifle musket are all that should usually be taken off or dismounted.

The soldier should never dismount the *band-springs, guard, side screw, washers, butt-plate, rear sight, cone,* and *cone-seat screw*, except when an officer considers it necessary. The breech screw should be taken out only by an armorer, and *never* in ordinary cleaning. The lock should not be taken apart, nor the bayonet-clasp taken off, except when absolutely necessary in the opinion of an officer. *If proper and regular care be taken of the arm, this will be very seldom necessary.*

The parts which are specially assigned to be dismounted by an experienced armorer will be stated in their regular order, following No. 10, viz:

11. Unscrew the cone, keeping the wrench well down on the square of the cone, to prevent the corners from being injured.

12. Take out the cone-seat screw.

13. Take out the upper, middle, and lower band-springs, using a wire punch of proper size.

14. Take out the side screws.*

15. Take out the guard, using care to prevent injuring the wood at each end of the guard-plate.

16. Take out the side screw washers with a drift punch.

17. Take out the butt-plate screws with the largest blade of the screw-driver, and remove the butt plate.

18. Remove the rear sight by turning out the leaf spring screw, which will release the sight from the barrel.

19. Turn out the breech screw by means of a " breech screw wrench" suited to the tenon of the breech screw. No other wrench should ever be used for this purpose, and the barrel should be held in clamps fitting neatly the breech.

Order in which the Lock is taken apart.

1. Cock the piece, and put the spring vice on the main spring; give the thumb screw a turn sufficient to liberate the spring from the swivel and main spring notch. Remove the spring.

2. The sear-spring screw. Before turning this screw entirely out, strike the elbow of the spring with the screw-driver, so as to disengage the pivot from its mortise; then remove the screw and spring.

3. The sear-screw and sear.

4. The bridle-screw and bridle.

---

* The guard, butt-plate, and side-screw heads have concave slits, for which the screw-driver is adapted: this lessens the danger of the stock being marred by accident or carelessness in letting the screw-driver slip out while in the act of turning the screw. Great care should be observed to prevent injury in this particular.

5. The tumbler-screw.

6. The tumbler. This is driven out with a punch inserted in the screw-hole, which at the same time liberates the hammer.

7. Detach the main-spring swivel from the tumbler with a drift-punch.

ASSEMBLING ARMS.

The lock and the musket are put together in the inverse order of taking them apart.

The Lock.

1. The main-spring swivel. 2. The tumbler and hammer. 3. The tumbler-screw. 4. Bridle and screw. 5. Sear and screw. 6. Sear-spring and screw. 7. Main spring.

Before replacing the screws, oil them slightly with good sperm oil, putting a drop on the point of the screw; also, on the arbor and pivot of the tumbler; between the movable branches of the springs and the lock-plate; on the hook and notches of the tumbler. After the lock is put together, avoid turning the screws in so hard as to make the limbs bind: to insure this, try the motion of each limb before and after its spring is mounted, and see that it moves without friction.

The Musket.

1. The barrel. Drop the barrel into its place in the stock, and squeeze it down with the hand; give the butt of the stock a gentle tap against the floor, to settle the breech end of the barrel against the head of the stock.

2. Put on the lower band with the letter U upward, being careful not to mar the stock or barrel in sliding it into its place; apply the thumb to the band-spring, to see that it plays freely.

3. Put on the middle band; and,

4. The upper band, in the same manner.

5. The lock. Half-cock the hammer; take the lock in the right hand, with the main spring and sear toward you, holding the stock with the left hand by the swell, with the butt between

the knees. Enter the lock fairly into the lock-bed, taking care to keep the arm of the sear clear of the trigger; press the plate well down into the wood, and then turn the musket over, holding the lock and stock together with the left hand.

6. With the right hand, turn in the side screws, after having touched their screw-threads with oil. Observe that the point of the rear screw is *flat*, and should not project beyond the plate, to interfere with the hammer. The front screw has a round point.

7. Turn in the tang-screw, after having oiled the screw-thread. Be careful to see that each of these screws are turned firmly home, *but not forced*. Observe that the lock plays freely, without friction, and that no limb is bound by the wood.

8. Return the ramrod.

9. Refix the bayonet, after having oiled the clasp and socket to prevent chafing.

10. Replace the tompion. *Oil the stock* well with sperm or linseed oil; let it stand a few hours, and then rub it with a woolen rag until the wood is perfectly dry. Repeat this from time to time, and it will produce a polish which moisture will not affect.

Linseed oil is the best for this purpose, and it should be used while the arm is dismounted.

CLEANING AND CARE OF ARMS.

To Clean the Barrel.

1. Stop the hole in the cone with a peg of soft wood; pour a gill of water (warm, if it can be had) into the muzzle; let it stand a short time, to soften the deposit of the powder; put a plug of soft wood into the muzzle, and shake the water up and down the barrel well; pour this out and repeat the washing until the water comes out clear; take out the peg from the cone, and stand the barrel, muzzle downward, to drain for a few moments.

2. Screw the wiper on to the end of the ramrod, and put a piece of *dry cloth* or *tow* round it, sufficient to prevent it from chafing the grooves of the barrel; wipe the barrel quite dry, changing or drying the cloth two or three times.

3. Put no oil into the vent, as it will clog the passage, and cause the first cap to miss fire; but, with a slightly oiled rag on the wiper rub the bore of the barrel and the face of the breech-screw, and immediately insert the tompion into the muzzle.

4. To clean the exterior of the barrel, lay it flat on a bench or board, to avoid bending it. The practice of supporting the barrel at each end and rubbing it with a strap or buff stick, or with the ramrod or any other instrument, *to burnish* it, is pernicious, and should be strictly forbidden.

5. After firing, the barrel should always be washed as soon as practicable; when the water comes off clear, wipe the barrel dry, and pass into it a rag moistened with oil.

As rust and dirt are produced by exploding caps or primers, although no charge be fired, the parts of the barrel and cone exposed should be carefully wiped and oiled after such practice.

Fine *flour of emery* cloth is the best article to clean the exterior of the barrel.

To Clean the Lock.

Wipe every part with a moist rag, and then a dry one; if any part of the interior shows rust, put a drop of oil on the point or end of a piece of soft wood dipped into flour of emery; rub out the rust clean and wipe the surface dry; then rub every part with a slightly oiled rag.

When a lock has, from any cause, become gummed with oil and dirt, it may be cleaned by being boiled in soap-suds or in pearlash or soda water, to loosen the thick oil; but heat should never be applied to any part of it in any other way.

To Clean the Mountings.

For the mountings, and all of the iron and steel parts, use fine flour of emery, moistened with oil, or flour of emery cloth.

For brass, use rotten-stone moistened with vinegar or water, and keep free from oil or grease. Use a hard brush, or a piece of soft pine, cedar, or crocus cloth.

Remove dirt from the screw-holes by screwing a piece of soft wood into them.

Wipe clean with a linen rag, and leave the parts slightly oiled.

In cleaning the arms, great care should be observed to *preserve the qualities essential to service,* rather than to obtain a bright polish.

Burnishing the barrel (or other parts) should be strictly avoided, as it tends to crook the barrel, and also to destroy the uniformity of the exterior finish of the arm.

It is not essential for the musket to be dismounted every time that it is cleaned; for, after firing it in fine weather, or when there has been no chance for the wet to get between the barrel and the stock, it can be perfectly cleaned in the following manner—

Put a piece of rag or soft leather on the top of the cone, and let the hammer down upon it; pour a gill of water into the muzzle, carefully, so that it does not run down the outside; put a plug of wood into the muzzle, and shake the gun up and down, changing the water repeatedly, until it comes out clear. When clear, withdraw the leather, and stand the musket on the muzzle for a few moments: then wipe out the barrel (as given in the second rule for cleaning), and also wipe the exterior of the lock and the outside of the barrel around the cone and cone-seat, first with a damp rag, and then with a dry one, and lastly with a rag that has been slightly oiled. In this way, all the dirt due to the firing may be removed without taking out a screw.

If, however, the hammer be observed to work stiff, or to grate upon the tumbler, the lock must immediately be taken off and the parts cleaned and touched with oil.

To change the cone, when it is broken or worn out.—After removing the old cone, enter the new one carefully with the fingers, before using the wrench, in order to avoid bruising the thread in the barrel.

It is very important to use no other implements than those before mentioned. By using nails to drive out the wires, their holes are enlarged. The main spring should never be heated for the purpose of either raising or lowering its temper; this destroys the elasticity of the spring, and the lock no longer gives fire.

The notches of the tumbler, the main spring, swivel, and in general, all the joints of the lock should be frequently oiled, after first wiping off the hard grease and the dust.

Browned arms are cleaned by rubbing them hard with an oiled rag until the oil is well incorporated with the browning, or by rubbing them with beeswax on a rag or cork.

Rifled arms should not have the *ramrod sprung* in the bore with unnecessary force. It batters the head of the rod, and wears injuriously the grooves. The soldier should let the rod slide down gently, supported by the thumb and finger; and the inspecting officer can satisfy himself of the condition of the bottom of the bore by gently tapping with the rod. The face of the breech can be polished, after washing, by means of a cork fixed on the wiper or ball-screw; the polished surface can be seen if the muzzle is turned to the light.

Besides all the precautions in dismounting, remounting and cleaning, which have been pointed out in the foregoing pages, habitual care in handling the arms is necessary to keep them in good and serviceable condition.

In *ordering arms* on parade, let the butt be brought gently to the ground, especially when the exercises take place on pavements or hard roads. This will save the mechanism of the lock from shocks, which are very injurious to it, and which tend to loosen and mar the screws and split the wood-work.

In *stacking arms*, care should be taken not to injure the bayonets by forcibly straining the edges against each other. The stack can be as well secured without such force being used.

No cutting, marking, or scraping in any way the wood or iron should be allowed; and no part of the gun should be touched with a file. Take every possible care to prevent water from getting in between the lock, or barrel and stock. If any should get there, dismount the gun as soon as possible, clean and oil the parts as directed, and see that they are perfectly dry before reassembling them.

Strength and Durability of Musket Barrels.

To test the strength of musket barrels, model 1855, they have been fired with an increasing number of cartridges, until the force of the explosion of the first two cartridges was unable to drive out the other charges, and the gas escaped through the vent, leaving the barrel uninjured.

The strength of the barrel, therefore, furnishes every requisite security against the accidents of service and the want of care on the part of the soldier.

Experience has shown that a musket barrel may be fired 25,000 times without becoming unserviceable.

Barrels which are condemned in service are almost always the result of accident, very rarely from enlargement of the bore or from the diminution of the exterior dimensions.

The following trials of the strength and durability of the French musket barrel are taken from the *Aide-Mémoire*. They refer to the smooth bore musket: It is to be observed that the charge of the French musket was formerly 162 grains Troy, priming included (or 146 grains, exclusive of priming), and is, therefore, considerably greater than our present service charge.

In experiments made in 1806, barrels reduced 0.13 inch at the breech bore a double and triple charge with one ball, or two cartridges placed one over the other.

Other trials were made in 1829, at the manufactory of Mutzig, on arms sent there for repairs, which had been a greater or less time in the hands of the troops. They furnished the following results—

1st. When a musket barrel is charged with a single cartridge, placed in any part of it, or with 2 or even with 3 cartridges, inserted regularly, without any interval·between them, there is no danger of bursting; with 4 cartridges inserted regularly over each other, or with 2 or even 3 cartridges placed over each other with slugged balls (or balls *driven* in, as in a rifle), there is danger only in case of some defect of fabrication, or some deterioration in the barrel; with more than 4 cartridges inserted regularly one over another, or with 2, 3 and 4 cartridges with intervals between them, it is not safe to fire.

Late experiments with the rifle musket show that any number of cartridges can be placed one upon the other, and the piece be fired without injury. In consequence of the expansive nature of the projectile, which cuts off the passage of the flame, but two charges will be inflamed, and their force will be expended through the vent.

2d. No danger of bursting is occasioned by leaving a ball screw in the barrel. There may be danger from a plug of wood driven tight into the muzzle, when the barrel has been loaded with 2 cartridges; or from a cork rammed into the barrel to a certain distance from the charge, with another cartridge over it.

Snow, clay and sand, which may be accidentally introduced into the barrel, are not dangerous, if they lie close to the charge; but they are so when there is a space between them and the charge; in this case sand is the most dangerous, then clay and snow.

Balls or pieces of iron inserted over the charge were not attended with danger when placed close to the charge, even when their weight amounted to $1\frac{1}{4}$ lb.; but there is danger from a piece of iron, 0.5 inch square, weighing $\frac{1}{4}$ lb., if placed 20 inches or more from the breech.

3d. A barrel with a defect which might have escaped the inspector at the armory, bore the explosion of 3 cartridges, regularly inserted. After mutilation, which may have caused a reduction of metal in some parts, it may still be used without danger.

Finally, the diminutions of exterior diameter which may be produced in ordinary service are never sufficient to be dangerous. In these trials, barrels originally 0.272 inch thick at the breech did not burst when loaded with 2 cartridges, until the thickness was reduced to 0.169 inch, and with 1 cartridge to 0.091 inch.

Spare Appendages required for the repair of 1,000 *Rifle Muskets during one year in the field.*

Wipers, - - - - -	75
Screw drivers, - - - -	25
Ball screws, - - - - -	25
Spring vices, - - - - -	25
Tompions, - - - - -	100
Band spring and tumbler punch, - - -	25

Spare Parts for 1000 *Rifles* (*Model* 1855) *one year in the field.*

	Nos.		Nos.
Barrels, - - - -	2	Guard-bows, - - -	20
Vent-screws, - - -	30	" nuts, - - -	40
Rear-sights, - - -	20	" " swivels and rivets,	50
Breech-screws, - - -	10	Triggers, - - -	10
Tang " - - -	30	" screws, - -	10
Cones, - - - -	50	Guard-plate screws, - -	50
Locks, - - - -	2	Butt-plates, - - -	2
Lock-plates, - - - -	5	" screws, - -	20
Hammers, - - - -	25	Box-plates with catches, -	5
Tumblers, - - - -	20	" screws, - -	10
" screws, - - -	100	" springs, - -	10
Bridles, - - - -	20	" " screws,	10
" screws, - - -	50	Ramrods, - - -	50
Sears, - - - -	20	" stops, - -	10
" screws, - - -	50	Stocks, - - -	30
Sear-springs, - - -	50	Screw-drivers, - -	50
" screws, - - -	50	Wipers, - - -	50
Main springs, - - -	50	Ball-screws, - -	10
" swivels, - -	40	Spring-vices, - -	10
" " rivets, -	40	Tumbler and wire punches, -	10
Side screws, - - -	100	Bullet-moulds, - -	5
Upper bands with swivels, -	10	Swages for balls, - -	5
" band swivels and rivets, -		Sword-bayonets, - -	30
" band springs, -	30	Tompions, - - -	20
Lower bands, - - -	10	Sword-bayonet lock-pins, -	25
" band springs, -	20	" " springs,	55
Side screw washers, -	30	" " spring	
Guard-plates, - - -	10	screws,	50

SWORDS AND SABRES.

Sabres are *curved*, and swords *straight.*

NOMENCLATURE.

Cavalry sabre consists of a curved *blade* 36 inches long, *hilt guard* and *scabbard* of *sheet steel.*

Mounted artillery sabre.—This differs from the cavalry sabre in having a *blade* only 32 inches long, though of greater curvature. It also has a *hilt, guard* and *scabbard.*

Foot artillery sword has a straight *two-edged blade* 19 inches long, narrower nearer the hilt than in the middle, a *hilt* and *leather scabbard.*

Infantry sword has a *blade* straight (cut and thrust) 32 inches in length, a *hilt, guard* and *leather scabbard.* This sword is for the non-commissioned officers of foot troops. The sword for officers not mounted is of the same pattern, with ornamented mountings.

Principal Dimensions and Weights of Swords and Sabres.

DIMENSIONS.	Cavalry Sabre.	Artillery Sabre.	Artillery Sword.	Infantry Sword.
	Inches.	Inches.	Inches.	Inches.
Whole length of thé sword or sabre in its scabbard, - - - -	43.25	38.6	26.	38.75
Length of the blade proper, - -	36.	32.	19.	32.
Length of the scabbard, -	37.25	33.	20.	32.5
Width of the blade in the middle, -	1.1	1.06	1.8	0.72
Versed sine of the curvature of the blade in the middle, - - -	1.5	2.32		
Versed sine of the curvature of the blade in proof, - - -	7.5	6.5	–	6.5
WEIGHTS.	Lbs. oz.	Lbs. oz.	Lbs. oz.	Lbs. oz.
Weight of the sword or sabre, complete,	4 8	4 1½	3 3	2 5
Weight of the finished blade, -	1 5	–	1 9	
Weight of the scabbard, -	2 2	–	10	

Cleaning Swords and Sabres.

The iron and brass parts of swords and sabres are cleaned in the same manner as those of muskets. When the oil on the blade of a sword is dried up, it will leave a spot which may be removed by covering it with oil and rubbing it smartly, after a short time, with a linen rag. When a leather scabbard has become wet, draw the blade and dry the scabbard slowly without heating it; wipe the blade dry and pass an oiled rag over it and the scabbard, before returning the blade. Oil the blades of arms in store, and also the scabbards, especially on the seams.

ACCOUTREMENTS.

Infantry Accoutrements.

Cartridge box, *cartridge-box plate* (brass), *cartridge-box belt, cartridge-box belt-plate, cap pouch, cone pick, bayonet scabbard, waist belt, waist-belt plate, gun-sling, sword-shoulder belt and plate,* for non-commissioned officers.

Rifle Accoutrements.

The same as for infantry accoutrements, except the *waist belt* for the sword bayonet and the *sword-bayonet scabbard.*

Cavalry Accoutrements.

Cartridge box for carbine, *pistol cartridge box, cartridge-box plate, cap pouch, cone pick, sabre belt, sabre-belt plate, sword knot, carbine sling, holsters.*

Mounted Artillery Accoutrements.

Sabre belt, sabre-belt plate, sword knot.

Foot Artillery Accoutrements.

Sword belt, belt-plate.

Weight of Accoutrements.

100 infantry cartridge-boxes and plates for .69-in. ball, -	176 lbs.
100 infantry cartridge-boxes and plates for .58-in. ball, -	167 "
100 infantry cartridge box belts and plates, - -	63 "
100 cap-pouches and cone-picks, - - -	13 "
100 bayonet scabbards and frogs, - - -	31 "
100 waist belts and plates, 1.9 inch wide, - -	50 "
100 gun slings, - - - - -	15 "
100 non-commissioned officer's waist belts and plates, -	49 "
100 non-commissioned officer's sword belts and plates (shoulder), - - - - -	60 "
100 rifle cartridge-boxes and plates for .54-in. ball, -	118 "
100 rifle waist belts and plates, for bayonet-scabbard, -	59 "
100 rifle sword-bayonet scabbards, - -	49 "
100 rifle pouches, - - - -	43 "
100 rifle flasks, - - - - -	81 "
100 rifle flask and pouch belts, - - -	27 "
100 cavalry sabre belts and plates, - -	120 "
100 carbine slings and swivels, - - -	110 "
100 light artillery sabre belts and plates, - -	95 "
100 foot artillery sword belts and plates, - -	81 "

MUSKET AND RIFLE PRACTICE.

Dangerous space.—In practice the object to be struck has a certain height, and the ball will strike it not only when it is at point plank, but also when it shall be at such points in rear or in front of the point blank, that the vertical distance of the trajectory from such points shall be equal to, or less than the height of the object. The distance between the points, where if a man were standing, he would be struck in the head, and where he would be struck in the feet, is called the *dangerous space*. For cavalry the *dangerous space* is greater than for infantry, for the same trajectory. The more *flattened* the trajectory, the greater the *dangerous space*.

The French rifle musket, at a distance of 273 yards, has a *dangerous space* of 87.5 yards; at 546 yards, of 42.5 yards; at 872 yards, of 20.5 yards.

For the *Enfield rifle musket* at 600 yards, the *dangerous space* is 60 yards; at 800, of 40 yards.

Comparative Efficacy of the Smooth Bored Musket, with Round Ball, and the Rifle, with the Hollow Ball.

Experiments were made in 1851, at Vincennes, to test the relative efficacy of the musket and rifle at various distances. The conclusions were as follows:

1st. In the fire by company, the rifle with the hollow ball has *no superiority* over the smooth bored musket with round ball, at 164 yards.

2d. At 218 yards, the rifle has *one and a half times* the efficacy.

3d. At 437 yards, the rifle has *six times* the efficacy.

4th. Beyond 437 yards, the musket has neither *accuracy* nor *penetration*, but the rifle has still very considerable efficacy.

Table showing the relative Penetration of Round and Cylindro-conic Balls.

437 yards.	Target 6 feet 6 inches.	NUMBER OF PLANKS.							
		1	2	3	4	5	6	7	8
Musket—round ball. 120 fired.	Struck, - - -	4	2						
	Penetrated, - -	2	1						
Tige rifle, cylindro-conic ball. 180 fired.	Struck, - - -	63	63	55	51	43	27	10	1
	Penetrated, - -	63	55	52	43	32	14	13	1

The planks were poplar, 1.02 inch thick, placed 18 inches in rear of each other. Charge of powder for round ball, 123.5 grains; cylindro-conic, 69.5 grains.

Mean deviations.—The following are the mean deviations of the rifle musket, fired from a shoulder and rest.

Distance.	Vertical.	Horizontal.	
Yards.	Inches.	Inches.	
100	1.9	1.5	
600	22.2	14.6	
1000	55.9	22.5	

Effect of bullets.—The penetration of the rifle musket bullet, in a target made of pine boards, one inch thick, are as follows:

At 200 yards, - - 11 inches.
" 600 " - - 6.33 "
" 1000 " - - 3.25 "

From experiments made in Denmark, the following relations were found between the penetration of a bullet in pine, and its effects on the body of a living horse, viz:

1st. When the force of the bullet is sufficient to penetrate 0.31 inch into pine, it is only sufficient to produce a slight contusion of the skin.

2d. When the force of penetration is equal to 0.63 inch, the wound begins to be dangerous, but does not always disable.

3d. When the force of penetration is equal to 1.2 inch, the wound is very dangerous.

It will thus be seen that the present bullet is capable of producing very dangerous wounds, at a much greater distance than 1,000 yards.

Accidents that occur with the Hollow Ball.

Projectiles, with a cavity in the base, are liable to be torn by the action of the gas, if it be too violent, or if the projectile be defective from its fabrication, as often occurs with moulded bullets. The tearing of hollow bullets is thus classified.

Lunettes.—In this case the cylindrical part of the bullet remains behind in the piece, the conical part being torn off by the action of the gas, and driven out without range or accuracy. In case of accidents of this kind, the arm is temporarily unfit for use, and has to be unbreeched to extract the *lunette.* Sometimes by forcing a second ball down point foremost, and ramming it hard against the *lunette*, they may both be fired out.

Anneaux : composed of a circular part of the hollow portion of the projectile, comprising one or more of the grooves; these accidents arise entirely from a defective fabrication.

Affouillements.—In this case the gas penetrates through the fissures or openings of the bullet, from defective moulding, and pierces without separating the front part of the bullet, thus driving it out with little force or accuracy.

CHAP. VII.

AMMUNITION.

GUNPOWDER.

Gunpowder should be of an even grain, angular and irregular in form; it should be so hard as not to be easily crushed by pressure with the finger; it should, when new, leave no trace of dust when poured on the back of the hand, and should leave no beads or foulness when flashed, in quantities of 10 grains, on a copper plate. It is distinguished as *musket, mortar, cannon* and *mammoth* powder. They are all made in the same manner, of the same proportion of materials, and differ only in the size of the grain.

Materials.—The materials required are saltpetre, charcoal and sulphur. They should be of the greatest possible purity.

Proportions of materials.—All powder for the military service must be composed of the following proportions, by weight, viz:

76 parts of nitre, 14 of charcoal and 10 of sulphur;
Or 75 " " 15 " 10 "

Size of grain.—The size of the grain is tested by standard sieves made of sheet brass pierced with round holes. Two sieves are used for each kind of powder: Nos. 1 and 2 for musket, 2 and 3 for mortar, 4 and 5 for cannon, and 6 and 7 for mammoth powder.

Diameter of holes for musket powder, No. 1, 0.03 in.; No. 2, 0.06 in.
" " mortar " No. 2, 0.06 in.; No. 3, 0.10 in.
" " cannon " No. 4, 0.25 in.; No. 5, 0.35 in.
" " mammoth " No. 6, 0.60 in.; No. 7, 0.90 in.

Musket powder.—None should pass through sieve No. 1—all through No. 2.

Mortar powder.—None should pass through sieve No. 2—all through No. 3.

Cannon powder.—None should pass through sieve No. 4—all through No. 5.

The smaller the grains of powder, to a certain limit, the more nearly instantaneous is its conversion into gas. The object of using large grained powder is to avoid its *instantaneous* conversion into gas, which would burst the gun. As a general rule, in firing cannon, the heavier the projectile the larger the grain of powder used, and conversely. The *inertia of rest* of the projectile is proportional to its mass, and a *small interval of time* is required to impart to it, with safety to the gun, the velocity with which it issues from the muzzle.

Powder Measures.

Made of sheet copper; those for use in the park should be made without handles, for the convenience of putting them up in a nest; their form is cylindrical, the interior diameter and height being equal.

To find the diameter and height of a cylinder to contain a given quantity of gunpowder: Multiply the weight in pounds by

38.2 for cannon powder
39.4 for musket or rifle powder $\Big\}$ of medium density,

and take the cube root of the product.

Dimensions of Powder Measures.

WEIGHT OF POWDER.		DIAMETER AND HEIGHT.	WEIGHT OF POWDER.		DIAMETER AND HEIGHT.
Lbs.	oz.	Inches.	Lbs.	oz.	Inches.
0	1	1.337	2	0	4.240
0	2	1.685	2	8	4.571
0	4	2.122	3	0	4.857
0	8	2.673	4	0	5.346
1	0	3.368	4	8	5.560
1	4	3.628	6	0	6.120
1	8	3.855	8	0	6.736

Ammunition for Small Arms now used in the C. S. Service.

	Calibre.	Weight of ball—grains.	Diameter of ball—inches.	Charges—grains.
Belgian rifle, - - -	.70	738	.675	80
Mississippi rifle, - -	.54	470	.525	70
Rifle musket, - - -	.69	738	–	80
Rifle " - - -	.58	500	.562	75
German rifle, - - -	.69	738	–	80
Enfield rifle, - -	.57	540	.562	70
Smooth bore musket (ball), -	.69	400	.650	100
" " " (buck and ball), -	.69	–.		110
English smooth bore musket, -	.75	480	–	110
Hall's carbine, - -	.54	228	–	60
Merrill's carbine, -	.56	430	–	50
Sharp's carbine, - -	.52	480	–	60
Burnside's carbine, -	.56	385	–	75
Colt's revolving carbine, -	.56	420	–	60
" " " -	.44	250	–.	35
Maynard's carbine, -	.51	345	–	55
" " -	.37	156	–	25
Colt's army pistol, -	.44	250	–	30
" navy " -	.33	145	–	17
Horseman's pistol, -	.54	228	–	30

How to make Cartridges.

When the cylinder of paper is not attached to the ball by the pressure of machinery closing the annulus around the base of the ball, as is usually done in the C. S. service, cartridges should be made with *thin wrappers.* The first, or inner paper envelope, is made by rolling with the hand the paper around a cylindrical mould, generally of wood, with a conical cavity at one end, to fit the cone of the ball. Besides this paper, a little rectangle of paste-board is also rolled, and the paper projecting beyond, pressed into the hollow of the mould, thus making a cylinder in which to receive the powder. The ball is then placed against the mould, *the point of the cone in the hollow of the mould,* and a *third wrap-*

per of thin, strong paper, in shape of a trapezoid, rolled and pasted around ball and powder. The cartridge is terminated by a compressed fold at the end with the powder, and tied with twine below the ball. The outer wrapper is then lubricated around the ball, with a mixture of two parts of bleached wax and one of tallow.

Buckshot cartridges have 4 tiers of 3 buckshot each, inserted like the first, with a half hitch between them, and finishing with a double hitch.

AMMUNITION FOR FIELD PIECES.

The charges of powder are contained in *cartridge bags*.

The projectile is attached to a block of wood called a *sabot*.

For the guns and the 12-pounder howitzer, the cartridge and the projectile are attached to the same sabot, making together *a round of fixed ammunition*.

For 32 *and* 24-*pounder howitzers*, the projectile is separate from the charge, and the cartridge is attached to a block of wood, called a *cartridge block*.

Charges of Powder.

KIND.	FOR GUNS.		FOR HOWITZERS.		
	12-pdr.	6-pdr.	32-pdr.	24-pdr.	12-pdr.
	Lbs.	Lbs.	Lbs.	Lbs.	Lbs.
For shot, - - - -	2.5	1.25			
For shell, - - - -	2.0	1.25	3.25	2.5	1.0
For spherical case, - - -	2.5	1.25	3.25	2.5	1.25
For canister, - - - -	2.0	1.0	2.5	2.0	1.0
For shell (large charge), - -	2.5				

Cartridge Blocks.

Cartridge blocks are cylinders of wood to which the cartridges of howitzers are attached, to give them a better finish, and to increase the length of the smaller charges, so that they may fill the chamber of the piece, and may be less apt to turn in the bore.

They are made of *poplar, linden,* or other soft wood.

Sabots.

Sabots are made of *poplar, linden* or other light, close grained wood. They should be clear of knots and splits, and well seasoned. They are made with a cavity to fit the ball, and a groove around which to tie the cartridge, thus serving as the means of connecting the charge with the projectile.

Fuze Plugs.

The fuzes for field shells and spherical case are inserted, at the moment of loading the gun, into wooden *fuze plugs*, previously driven into the shells.

These plugs are made of *beech*, perfectly seasoned and dried, so that they may not shrink after they are driven.

Charging Shells.

CHARGES.		32-pdr.		24-pdr.		12-pdr.		REMARKS.
		Lbs.	oz.	Lbs.	oz.	Lbs.	oz.	
Power required	to fill the shell, -	1	5	1		0	8	Rifle or musket powder is used in preference to cannon powder.
	to burst the shell, -	0	11	0	8	0	5	
	to blow out the fuze plug, -	0	2	0	2	0	1	
	for service charge,	1		0	12	0	7	

Spherical Case Shot.

CHARGE.		8-in.	42	32	24	18	12	6
Number of musket balls, -	-	486	306	225	175	120	78	38
Bursting charge of powder,	oz.	15	· 9	8	6	5	4.5	2.5
Weight of shot loaded,	- Ibs.	59.5	39.	30.13	22.75	16.3	11.	2 5

Cylinders and caps.—For the greater security of field ammunition, the cartridges are covered with paper cylinders and caps. The cap is drawn off at the moment of loading the piece, and in using solid shot it may be placed over the shot to diminish windage.

Dimensions and Weight of Fixed Ammunition.

DIMENSIONS.			FOR GUNS.		FOR HOWITZERS.		
			12	6	32	24	12
			In.	In.	In.	In.	In.
Height of charge of powder, including cartridge blocks for 32 and 24-pdr. howitzers.	Large charge,	-	5.	4.	7.4	5.9	3.25
	Small charge,	-	4.	3.25	7.4	5.4	
Height of strapped shot or shell,		-	5.02	4.13	7.14	6.58	6.42
Height of canister with sabot,	-	-	8.	6.75	10.5	9.55	8.75
Height of round of fixed ammunition.	Shot,	-	10.4	8.43			
	Shell,	-	–	–	–	–	10.
	Spherical case,	-	9.5	7.8	–	–	10.
	Canister,	-	12.4	10.3	–	–	12.3
WEIGHTS.			Lbs.	Lbs.	Lbs.	Lbs.	Lbs.
Cartridge, including cartridge block.	Large charge,	-	2.56	1.3	3.88	2.7	
	Small charge,	-	2.06	1.05	3.1	2.34	1.05
Shot, strapped,	-	-	12.75	6 28			
Shell, strapped and charged,	-	-	–	–	24.6	18.8	9.35
Spherical case, strapped and charged,		-	11 43	5.75	31.	23.	11.3
Canister with sabot,	-	-	14.8	7 32	28.5	21.25	10.8
Round of ammunition, complete.	Shot,	-	15 4	7.6			
	Shell, with small charge,	-	–	–	27.7	21.15	10.5
	Spherical case,	-	13 5	6.82	34.1	25.34	12.5
	Canister,	-	16.91	8.4*	31 6	23.6	11.85

Contents of each Packing Box for Field Ammunition.

KIND OF AMMUNITION.	FOR GUNS		KIND OF AMMUNITION.	HOWITZERS.		
	12-pdr.	6-pdr.		32-pdr.	24-pdr.	12-pdr.
Shot.			*Shells.*			
Shot fixed, - - -	8	14	Shells fixed, - -	—	—	12
Priming tubes, - -	5	5	Shells strapped, -	4	6	
Portfires, - - -	1	1	Cartridges, { small charge,	4	6	
Slow match, yards,	1.5	1.5	{ large charge,	1	1	
Spherical Case.			Priming tubes, - -	3	3	5
Shot fixed, - - -	8	14	Portfires, - -	1	1	1
Priming tubes, - -	5	5	Slow match, yards,	1.5	1.5	1.5
Portfires, - - -	1	1	Fuzes, { black, 2 sec. -	2	2	6
Slow match, yards,	1.5	1.5	{ red, 3 sec. -	4	6	12
Fuzes, { black, 2 sec. -	3	7	{ green, 4 sec. -	2	2	6
{ red, 3 sec. -	8	14	{ yellow, 5 sec. -	2	2	
{ green, 4 sec. -	3	7	*Spherical Case.*			
{ yellow, 5 sec. -	3		Shot fixed, - -	—	—	12
Canister.			Shot strapped, - -	4	6	
Canisters fixed, - -	8	14	Cartridges, small charge,	4	6	
Priming tubes, - -	5	5	Priming tubes, - -	3	3	5
Portfires, - - -	1	1	Portfires, - -	1	1	1
Slow match, yards,	1.5	1.5	Slow match, yards,	1.5	1.5	1.5
			Fuzes, { black, 2 sec. -	2	2	6
			{ red, 3 sec. -	4	6	12
			{ green, 4 sec. -	2	2	6
			{ yellow, 5 sec. -	2	2	
			Canister.			
			Canisters fixed, - -	—	—	12
			Canisters with sabots, -	4	6	
			Cartridges, small charge,	4	6	
			Priming tubes, - -	3	3	5
			Portfires, - -	1	1	1
			Slow match, yards,	1.5	1.5	1.5

AMMUNITION FOR SIEGE AND GARRISON SERVICE.

Cartridges.

The ordinary service charge of powder for heavy guns is *one-fourth* the weight of the shot; but the charge varies according to circumstances, from *one-third* the weight of the shot (for a breaching battery), to *one-sixth* of that weight, for firing double shot or hot shot, and still less, for ricochet firing. The charges for mortars and howitzers vary according to the required range.

Cartridge bags for siege and garrison service are usually made of woollen stuff. These are cut in two pieces, in the form of a rectangle with semicircular ends, which are sewed together to form the bag. See Ord. Manual, for the manner of making them.

Charges for Shells for Columbiads and heavy Guns.

CHARGE OF POWDER.	COLUMBIADS.		GUNS.				
	10-in.	8-in.	42	32	24	18	12
	Lbs. oz.	Lbs. oz.	Lbs. oz.	Lbs. oz.	Lbs. oz.	Lbs. oz.	Lbs. oz.
To fill the shell, -	3 4	1 12	1 8	1 5	1 0	0 11	0 8
To burst the shell, -	1 6	1 0	0 12	0 11	0 8	0 7	0 5
To blow out the fuze plug, - -	0 10	0 8	0 6	0 2	0 2	0 1½	0 1
For ordinary service,	3 0	1 8	1 4	1 0	0 12	0 10	0 7

The *fuzes* for these shells are made with paper cases, and are inserted at the time of loading the piece.

The *fuze plugs* are made of wood, or of brass, driven or screwed into the fuze hole; they are covered with a cap of peculiar construction which contains the priming of the fuze. The size of the plug is indicated by that of the fuze hole in the shell.

The bursting charge is poured into the shell through the hole in the fuze plug.

Wads.

Wads for proving cannon are made out of *junk*.

Wads for firing hot shot, and other like purposes, may be made of *hay*, wrapped with rope yarn; they are fabricated in the same manner as junk wads.

Ring wads (or *grommets*, as they are called in the naval service) have been found very serviceable in increasing the accuracy of fire, and they are to be preferred where the object of a wad is merely to retain the ball in its place. They consist of a ring of rope yarn, about 0.7 in. thick, with two pieces of strong twine tied across it, at right angles with each other. The size of the ring is the full diameter of the bore, in order that it may fit tight. These wads may be attached with twine to the straps, or to the balls; or, they may be inserted, like other wads, after the ball.

Military Fireworks.

Preparation for the service of ammunition are *slow-match, quick-match, port-fires, priming tubes, friction primers* and *fuzes.*

Slow-Match.

Slow-match is made of hemp, flax, or cotton rope, about 0.6 in. diameter, made with 3 strands, slightly twisted. Cotton rope, well twisted, forms a good match without any preparation.

To prepare hemp or flax rope: boil it 10 minutes in water holding in solution 1-20th of its weight of sugar of lead, or let it remain in the *cold* solution until it is thoroughly saturated—run it through the hands, or take the water from it, and twist it hard.

Match thus prepared, burns 4 inches in an hour. Cotton match burns 4½ inches in an hour.

Quick-Match.

Quick-match is made of cotton yarn—such as is used for candle-wick, by steeping it in gummed brandy or whiskey, and then soaking it for three or four hours in a paste made of mealed powder and gummed spirits. When dry it should be hard and stiff. One yard burns in the open air in 13 seconds.

Port Fires.

A *port fire* is a paper case containing a composition of 6 parts of nitre, 3 of sulphur and 1 of mealed powder, the flame of which is capable of quickly igniting primers, quick-match, &c. It is 22 inches long, and burns with an intense flame for ten minutes.

Priming Tubes.

Priming tubes are small metallic tubes filled with a paste of mealed powder and spirits of wine, to which is attached a small strand of quick-match. When the tube is made of a quill, they are called *quill tubes.* They are used for priming cannon.

Friction Primers.

A *friction primer* for cannon consists of a tube charged with gunpowder, to the top of which at right angles is attached a smaller tube containing friction powder, which is exploded by means of a serrated wire drawn out with a lanyard.

Friction powder is composed of two parts of *chlorate of potash* and one of *sulphuret of antimony*, moistened with alcohol, and mixed together in a wet state.

Lanyard.—The lanyard for pulling off the primers is a piece of strong cord; to one end is attached a small *iron hook*, and to the other a *wooden toggle*.

Fuzes.

Fuzes are the means used to ignite the charge of a hollow projectile at any desired moment of its flight; they are classified into *time*, *concussion* and *percussion fuzes*.

Time fuze.—This fuze is composed of a case of paper, wood or metal, enclosing a column of burning composition, which is set on fire by the discharge of the piece, and which, after burning a certain time, communicates with the bursting charge. Its successful operation depends on the *certainty of ignition, uniformity of burning*, and the *certainty of communicating the flame* to the bursting charge. The ingredients of the fuzes are the same as for gunpowder, but the proportions are varied to suit the required rate of burning. Pure mealed powder gives the quickest composition. There are two kinds of time fuzes used for field service—the *paper fuze* and the *Bormann fuze*.

Paper fuze.—This consists of a *paper case*, which is charged with the fuze composition being driven firmly in. Sometimes it is inserted, by two or three light blows with a wooden mallet, at the time of loading the gun, into a *wooden plug* previously driven into the fuze hole. If the fuze is inserted in the laboratory, over the top is fastened a disk of varnished paper to protect it, on which is inscribed the number of seconds that the fuze will burn. The paper is removed at the time of loading.

FUZE COMPOSITION.	MEALED POWDER.	SULPHUR.	TIME OF BURN- ING 1 INCH.
1	1	0.	2 seconds.
2	8	3.	3 "
3	8	3.5	4 "
4	8	4 0	5 "

In the *mortar fuze* the composition is driven into the wooden plug bored out nearly to the bottom, without the use of paper. The exterior of the plug is divided into inches and tenths. By cutting it off, the time of burning is regulated. The *seacoast fuze* has a brass plug and a metal cap, to prevent the ingress of water.

Bormann fuze.—This fuze is an invention of Capt. Bormann of the Belgian service, and is the only one used in the field at present in the C. S. service, for firing shell and spherical case from smooth bored guns.

The case is made of an alloy of tin and lead. Its shape is that of a thick circular disk, with a screw thread cut upon its edge, by which it is fastened into the fuze hole of the projectile. The upper surface is marked with an arc graduated into seconds and quarter seconds, under which is a circular groove filled with mealed powder. The only outlet to the groove containing the powder, is under the zero of the graduation; and this outlet is filled with rifle powder, which communicates with the bursting charge. The upper coating of metal is cut with a knife or gouge at the time of loading. If the fuzes become loose by the effects of transportation, they should be well tightened with a *fuze wrench*, and the edge around the fuze well glazed with a mixture of equal parts of litharge and white lead.

In the *paper fuze* the pressure is applied at the direction of the axis; and hence the mixture is not uniformly dense, while in the *Bormann fuze* the pressure is at right angles to the axis of the mixture, which renders it homogeneous, and thus produces great uniformity in burning.

Concussion fuze.—This operates by the shock of the discharge, or by that experienced in striking an object. One of the most celebrated is that invented by Capt. Splingard of the Belgian service. It has a tube of plaster of paris, surrounded by the composition. As the composition burns, the tube is left unsupported, and is broken by the shock of impact, when the flame of the composition immediately communicates with the bursting charge. None are adopted in the C. S. service.

Percussion fuze.—This explodes by the striking of some particular point of the projectile against an object, and is universally used with rifle cannon projectiles. The fuze adopted, has a moveable cone piece, bearing a musket cap, covered by a brass safety cap, which screws into the fuze hole. When the projectile is set in motion, the cone piece, by its inertia, presses against the shoulders of the fuze hole; when its motion is arrested, the momentum of the cone piece causes the percussion cap to impinge against the safety cap, which produces explosion. Mealed powder is sometimes introduced in the cavity of the cone piece to cause the explosion of the shell to take place after the explosion of the cap. The cone piece is held in its position by a piece of wire passing through the safety cap, and renders the shell safe in transportation. This wire is withdrawn at the instant of loading.

Rockets.

War rockets.—A rocket is a projectile which is set in motion by a power residing within itself, by the pressure of the escaping gas, in the direction opposite from that in which it escapes. It performs the part both of a piece and a projectile. The cases for *war rockets* are made of sheet iron, and lined with paper or wood veneer, to prevent the composition from touching the metal and rusting it. They are filled with a composition of nitre, sulphur and charcoal. At the top end either a solid shot or shell is placed. When the composition burns out, fire is communicated to the fuze, which explodes the charge in the shell. Two kinds of rockets have been used—*Congreve's and Hale's.*

Congreve's rocket has, like the ordinary skyrocket, a directing stick; but instead of being tied to the outside of the case, it is inserted in the rocket, and placed directly in the axis of the case, the flame escaping through holes around it. Sir William Congreve was the first who made use of metallic cases, but was not the inventor of the rocket. These rockets have been made of immense size, the largest weighing as much as three hundred pounds, but have never been adopted to any great extent.

Hale's rocket differs from any other, in having no guide stick Direction is given to it by imparting the *rifle* motion to it. This is effected by placing in the rear a number of escape holes oblique to the axis; the *inequality of pressure* caused in the escape of the gas produces a rotary motion.

War rockets are usually fired from tubes or troughs mounted on portable stands.

Signal rockets.—The principal parts of a signal rocket are the *case*, the *composition*, the *pot*, the *decorations*, the *stick*.

The *case* is made of several layers of stout paper pasted together.

The *composition* varies: 12 nitre, 2 sulphur, 3 charcoal is used, and for brilliancy, steel filings are added.

The *pot* is formed of a paper cylinder slipped over and pasted to the top of the case; it is surmounted with a paper cone filled with tow. The object of the *pot* is to contain the decorations, which are scattered through the air by the explosion which takes place when the rocket reaches the summit of its trajectory.

The decorations of rockets are *stars, serpents, marrons, gold rain, &c.*

Serpents are made of small paper cases like a rocket.

Marrons are small paper shells filled with grained powder.

The stick.—The stick is a tapering piece of pine about nine times the length of the case, and is tied to the side of the case to guide the rocket in its flight.

Incendiary Fire-works.

Fire stone is a composition that burns slowly but intensely; it is placed in a shell along with the bursting charge, for the purpose of setting fire to ships, buildings, &c. It is composed of 10 parts nitre, 4 sulphur, 1 antimony, 3 resin.

Carcass.—A carcass is a hollow cast iron projectile filled with burning composition, the flame of which issues through four fuze holes, to set fire to combustible objects. The composition is the same as for *port fires*, mixed with a small quantity of finely chopped tow, and as much *white turpentine* and *spirits of turpentine* as will give it proper consistency.

A common shell may be loaded as a carcass, by placing the bursting charge in the bottom of the cavity, and covering it with carcass composition, well driven in, and inserting four or five strands of quick-match.

Hot shot.—The precautions to be observed in loading hot shot, are, that the cartridge be perfectly tight, so that the powder shall not scatter along the bore, and that a wad of pure clay, or hay soaked in water, be interposed between the cartridge and the shot.

Fire Balls.

Fire balls are projectiles of an oval shape formed of sacks of canvas, filled with combustible composition. They are used to light up the enemy's works and are loaded with shells, to prevent them from being approached.

The sacks are made of strong and close canvas (sail cloth), which may be cut straight and gathered at the ends; or more neatly, cut in three gores or curved pieces, to form a ball. They are made of two or three thicknesses of stuff, according to its strength, and the pieces are sewed together with strong thread.

Light Balls.

Light balls are made in the same manner as fire balls, except that there is no shell in them, as they are used for lighting up our own works.

Tarred Links (*Tourteaux*),

Are used for lighting up a rampart, or for incendiary purposes. They consist of coils of soft rope placed on top of each other and loosely tied together; the exterior diameter is 6 inches, the interior 3 inches. They may be made of pieces of slow match about 15 feet long; immerse them for 10 minutes in a composition of 20 pitch and 1 tallow, and shape them under water; when dry, plunge them in a composition of equal parts of pitch and rosin, and roll them in tow or saw dust. In making them, the hands of the workmen should be covered with linseed oil.

A *link* takes from 1 lb. to 1¼ lb. of composition and ½ lb. of tow. Two of them are put into a rampart grate, separated by shavings. They burn one hour in calm weather, half an hour in a high wind, and are not extinguished by rain. The grates are placed about 250 feet apart.

Pitched Fascines.

Fagots of vine twigs, or other very combustible wood, about 20 inches long and 4 inches in diameter, tied in three places with iron wire, may be treated in the same manner as *links*, and used for the same purpose; their inflammability is increased by dipping the ends in melted fire stone.

STORAGE AND PRESERVATION OF AMMUNITION AND FIRE WORKS.

Leaden balls are generally kept in cellars, on account of their weight; the boxes should be kept as dry as possible, and so piled as to admit the circulation of air about them.

Cartridges for small arms are kept in magazines; the barrels or boxes being piled 3 or 4 tiers high at most. If barrels or boxes are not at hand, lay the bundles flat on a tarpaulin and pile them 10 high.

Fixed ammunition for cannon.—If not in boxes, it should be placed in piles formed of two parallel rows of cartridges, with the sabots together; in 4 tiers for 12-pounder, and 5 for 6-pounder; chock the lower tier with strips of wood fastened with small nails; put a layer of tow 2 inches thick between the shot; let the piles rest on planks, if there is no floor, and cover them with tarpaulins; have the place swept, and the cartridge bags brushed off. Leave a passage of 18 inches between the double rows, and keep them 2 feet from the walls.

Fixed ammunition should not be put into powder magazines, if it can be avoided; it should be kept in a dry place, above the ground floor if practicable; the store rooms should be always aired in fine weather; the piles should be taken down and made up again every six months at most, the bags examined and repaired, and the damaged cartridges broken up. A ticket on each pile should show the number and kind of cartridges, the additions to the pile, and the issues.

Canisters.—Piled up like fixed ammunition, in 4 tiers for 24's and 18's; and 5, for 12's and 6's. Empty canisters in 10 or 12 tiers; the bottoms and covers separately.

Cartridge bags filled.—Like fixed ammunition or packed in boxes or barrels.

Paper cartridge bags.—In bundles, packed in boxes or on shelves, in a dry place, with the precautions before indicated against worms and moths.

Loaded shells should never be put into magazines, except from absolute necessity; powder is not well preserved in them. They should be piled on the ground floor of a secure building—on planks, if the floor is not boarded; in 6 tiers at most; the fuzes of the lower tier in the vacant spaces between the shells; those of the other tiers turned downward, like the fuze holes of empty shells; the pile should be covered with a tarpaulin.

Slow-match.—In a dry place, such as a garret.

Quick-match.—If not in boxes, it may be hung up in bundles, on ropes or pins, and covered with paper.

Priming tubes, port-fires, fuzes, signal rockets.—In safe and dry situations, packed in boxes.

Fire balls.—In a cool place, separated from each other by shavings or straw, if they are piled up.

Tarred links.—Strung on a rope and hung up; for transportation they are packed in barrels, with straw between the tiers.

Fascines and torches.—Packed like the preceding.

Fire stone and incendiary compositions should not be kept in large quantities.

Percussion primers, in cool, dry places, apart from gunpowder and ammunition. Some cannon primers have exploded under circumstances which led to the opinion that their combustion was spontaneous. They should be carefully protected from rats, etc., by being enclosed in glass or tin.

CHAP. VIII.

EQUIPMENT OF BATTERIES FOR FIELD SERVICE.

EQUIPMENT OF FIELD BATTERIES.

Interior Arrangement of Ammunition Chests for Field Guns and Howitzers.

The principal divisions of a chest are designated as the *right half* and the *left half*, to a person facing the front of the chest.

The smaller divisions in each half, perpendicular to the sides, are designated as *first, second, third,* &c., from the principal partition, each way; the divisions parallel to the sides are designated as the *front, middle* and *rear divisions.*

The kind of ammunition contained in the small divisions is marked on the inside of the cover, over each division.

Ammunition carried in each Chest.

KIND.	No.	Weight.	PLACE.
FOR 6-POUNDER GUN.		Lbs.	
Shot, fixed, - - -	25	190.	In the left half.
Spherical case, fixed, -	20	140.	In the 1st four divisions of right half.
Canisters, fixed, - -	5	42.	In 5th division, right half.
Spare cartridges, 1¼ lb. -	2	2.6	On the spherical case.
Friction primers, - -	75	.97	In a tin box, in the tray.
Slow match, yard,	2	.38	⎫ On the ammunition in right half.
Portfires, - - -	2	.57	⎭
Total number of rounds, -	50		
		376.52	
FOR 12-POUNDER GUN.			
Shot, fixed, - - -	20	308.	In left half, and in 4th division of right half.
Spherical case, fixed, -	8	117.6	In 1st and 2d divisions, right half.
Canisters, fixed, - -	4	67.64	In 3d division, right half.
Spare cartridges, 2½ lbs. -	2	5.12	On the spherical case.
Friction primers, - -	48	.62	In a tin box, in the tray.
Slow match, *l* yard,	1.5	.28	⎫ On the ammunition in right half.
Portfires, - - -	2	.57	⎭
Total number of rounds, -	32		
		499.83	
FOR 12-POUNDER GUN (NAPOLEON).			
Shot, fixed, - - -	12	184.8	In 1st, 2d and 3d divisions, left half.
Spherical case, - -	12	176.4	In 1st, 2d and 3d divisions, right half.
Shells, - - -	4	48.68	In 4th division, right half.
Canisters, - - -	4	67.64	In 4th division, left half.
Spare cartridges, 2.5 lbs. -	2	5.12	On the shells.
Friction primers, - -	48	.62	In a tin box, in the tray.
Slow match, yard,	1.5	.28	⎫ On the ammunition in right half.
Portfires, - - -	3	.57	⎭
Total number of rounds, -	32		
		484.11	
FOR 12-PDR. HOWITZER.			
Shells, fixed, - -	15	157.5	In 2d, 3d and 4th divisions, right half.
Spherical case, fixed, -	20	273.	In left half.
Canisters, fixed, - -	4	47.4	In 1st division, right half.
Friction primers, - -	58	.75	In a tin box on the canisters.
Slow match, yards,	2	.38	⎫ On the canisters.
Portfires, - - -	2	.57	⎭
Total number of rounds, -	39		
		479.6	

Ammunition carried in each Chest—Continued.

KIND.	No.	Weight.	PLACE.
FOR 24-PDR. HOWITZER.		Lbs.	
Shells, strapped, - -	12	225.60	In left half.
Spherical case, strapped, -	8	214.92	In front and middle divisions of right half.
Canisters, - - -	3	63.75	In rear divisions of right half.
Cartridges. { Small charge,	23	53.82	12 in middle division, left half; 9 in middle division, right half; 2 on the canisters.
{ Large charge,	2	5.40	On canisters.
Friction primers, - -	34	.44	In a tin box on the canisters.
Slow match, yard,	1	.19	} On the canisters.
Portfires, - - -	2	.57	
Total number of rounds, -	23		
		564.69	
FOR 32-PDR. HOWITZER.			
Shells, strapped, - -	8	196.80	Front and rear divisions of left half.
Spherical case, strapped, -	6	216.00	Rear divisions and right front division of right half.
Canister, - - -	1	28.50	Left front division, right half.
Cartridges. { Small charge,	15	46.50	} 1st division in each half.
{ Large charge,	1	3.88	
Friction primers, - -	22	.28	In a tin box in the middle division.
Slow match, . yard,	.5	.09	} In the middle division.
Portfires, - - -	1	.28	
Total number of rounds, -	15		
		492.33	
FOR MOUNTAIN HOWITZER.			
Shells, fixed, - -	1	9.9	In left end.
Spherical case, fixed, -	6	75.6	In middle.
Canisters, fixed, -	1	11.8	In right end.
Friction primers, - -	12	.15	In water proof paper.
Slow match, yard,	½	.09	
Portfires, - - -	1	.28	
Total number of rounds, -	8		
		97 82	

FOR PRAIRIE HOWITZER.—The same as for the mountain howitzer.

Implements and Equipments for Field Carriages.

KIND.	No.	Weight.	PLACE.
FOR A GUN OR HOWITZER CARRIAGE.		Lbs.	
Sponges and rammers, -	2		
Sponge covers, - -	2	0.24	
Worm and staff, - -	½	3.6	
Handspikes, - -	2	14.5	} On the gun carriage.
Sponge bucket, - -	1	10.	
Prolonge, - -	1-	12.5	
Vent cover, - -	1	0.2	On the gun.
Tar bucket, - -	1	7.	} On the limber.
Water bucket (leather), -	2	16.	
Gunner's haversacks, -	2	3.72	
Tube pouch, - -	2	1.80	In the implement trays, or in other
Vent punch, - -	1	0.08	vacant spaces in the ammunition
Gunner's pincers, -	1	0.85	chest.
Tow hook, - -	1	0.60	
Hausse, - -	1	0.65	
Thumb stalls, : -	2	0 01	
Priming wire, - -	1	0.08	} In the tube pouch.
Lanyard for friction primers,	2	0.20	
Gunner's gimlet, - -	1	0.08	} In the tube pouch.
Fuze cutter, - -	1	0.2	
Tarpaulin, large, - -	1	37.75	Strapped on the ammunition chest.
FOR A CAISSON.			
Felling axe, - -	1	6.	
Shovel, long handle, -	1	4.75	
Pickaxe, - -	1	6.5	In the places provided for them on the
Spare handspike, -	1	7.25	caisson body.
Spare pole, - -	1	25.30	
Spare wheel, - -	1	180.	
Tow hooks, - -	2	1.2	One in the limber chest, and one in a caisson chest.
Tar bucket, - -	1	7.	} On the limber.
Watering bucket (leather),	2	16.	
Tarpaulin, large, - -	1	37.75	Strapped on the limber chest.

Implements and Equipments for Prairie Carriages.

KIND.	No.	Weight.	PLACE.
		Lbs.	
Sponges and rammers, -	2	3.	} On the carriage.
Sponge covers, - -	2	2.3	
Handspike, - -	1	5.	
Vent cover, - -	1	.18	On the gun.
Haversack, - -	1	1.86	} In ammunition chests.
Tube pouch, - -	2	1.80	
Priming wire, • -	1	0.08	
Thumb stalls, - -	2	.01	} In the tube pouch.
Gunner's gimlet, - -	1	0.08	
Lanyard for friction primers,	2	0.2	
Fuze cutter, - -	1	0.2	
Gunner's pincers, - -	1	0.85	In tool chest A.
Tarpaulin, 6x10 feet, -	1	12.25	On the ammunition chest.
Water bucket, - -	1	8.	On the limber.
Prolonge, - -	1	–	On the gun carriage.
Tar bucket, - -	1	7.	On the limber.

Implements and Equipments for the Mountain Howitzer Carriage.

KIND.	No.	Weight.	PLACE.
		Lbs.	
Handspike, - •	1	5.0	} On the carriage.
Sponge and rammer, -	1	3.0	
Sponge cover, - -	1	.11	On the sponge.
Vent cover, - -	1	0.18	On the gun.
Haversack, - •	1	1.86	On the pack with the ammunition
Tube pouch, • -	2	1.80	} chests.
Priming wire, - -	1	0.08	
Gunner's gimlet, - -	1	0.08	} In the tube pouch.
Lanyard for friction primers,	2	0.2	
Fuze cutter, - -	1	0.2	In ammunition chest.
Gunner's pincers, - -	1	0.85	In tool chest A.
Tarpaulin, 5x5 feet, -	1	5.25	On the pack with the ammunition chest.

EQUIPMENT OF TRAVELLING FORGES AND BATTERY WAGONS.

One forge and one battery wagon accompany each field battery. They are furnished with the tools and materials required for shoeing horses and for ordinary repairs and preservation of carriages and harness.

Other forges and battery wagons, equipped for the general service of the army, accompany the field park which contains the general supplies of ordnance stores.

The forge for the field battery is designated by the letter A.
The forge for the field park " " " B.
The battery wagon for the field battery " " " C.
The battery wagon for the field park " " " D.

EQUIPMENT OF A FORGE FOR A FIELD BATTERY.

Limber Chest.

The chest is marked FORGE A. The stores and tools are carried in 6 *boxes* and 1 *oil can.*

The boxes are marked, respectively, A, Nos. 1, 2, 3, 4, 5.

Contents of the Limber Chest of Forge A.

Smith's Tools and Stores.	No.	Weight.	Smith's Tools and Stores.	No.	Weight.
		Lbs.			Lbs.
Box A 1, containing:	–	8.25	Box A 5, containing:	–	14.5
Horseshoes Nos. 2 and 3, -	90	100.	Fire shovel, -	1	3 05
			Poker, -	1	1.90
Box A 2, containing:	–	9.75	Split broom, -	1	1.25
Horseshoe nails Nos. 2			Hand hammer, -	1	3.50
and 3, -	–	50.00	Riveting hammer, -	1	1.05
Washers and nuts No. 2, -	30	5.25	Nailing hammer, -	1	1.80
Washers and nuts No. 3, -	10	3.20	Sledge hammer, -	1	10.50
Washers and nuts No. 4, -	4	2.15	Chisels for hot iron, -	2	3.00
Nails No. 1 C, -	–	1.00	Chisels for cold iron, -	2	3.00
Nails No. 2 C, -	–	1.00	Smith's tongs, -	3	15.00
Tire bolts, -	20	5.00	Fore punch, -	1	1.00
Keys for ammunit'n chests,	5	1.80	Creaser, -	1	1.00
Linch washers, -	8	7.30	Fuller, -	1	2.40
Linch pins, -	12	8.37	Nail claw, -	1	5.00
Chains Nos. 1 and 2, ft.	2	1.54	Round punch, -	1	2.10
Coldshut S-links, No. 3, -	50	2.50	Tap wrench, -	1	3.75
Coldshut S-links, No. 5, -	12	2.00	Die stock, -	1	6.25
Total contained in Box			Nave bands, developed,	4	11.75
A 2, -	–	91.11	Tire bands, developed, -	2	2.75
			Total contained in Box		
Box A 3, containing:	–	8.25	A 5, -	–	80.05
Horseshoes Nos. 2 and 3, -	90	100.00			
			Shoeing box, containing:	–	4.7
Box A 4, containing:	–	8.0	Shoeing hammer, -	1	0.82
Hand cold chisels, -	2	2.00	Pincers, pair,	1	2.00
Hardie, -	1	0.75	Rasps (12 inches), -	2	2.15
Files assorted, with handles,	12	10.00	Shoeing knife, -	1	0.33
Buttress, -	1	1.50	Toe-knife, -	1	0.30
Hand punches, round and			Pritchel, -	1	0.85
square, -	2	2.00	Nail punch, -	1	0.80
Screw wrench, -	1	2.42	Clinching iron, -	1	1.00
Hand screw driver, -	1	0.32	Oil stone, -	1	1.50
Hand vise, -	1	1.00	Leather aprons, -	2	3.00
Smith's callipers, pair,	1	0.40	Total contained in shoe-		
Taps, Nos. 1, 2, 3,	4	1 50	ing box, -	–	12.75
Dies, pairs, and 4, -	4	1.83			
Wood screws, 1 in. No. 14, groce,	1	2.10	Iron square, in clamps on		
			the inside of cover,	1	2.00
Quart can of sperm oil, -	1	2.70	Padlock, on chest,	1	0.50
Total contained in Box			Tow, used in packing, -	–	5.00
A 4, -	–	28.52	Tar-bucket, on its hook,	1	7.00
			Total, -	–	480.38

Boxes Nos. 1, 2 and 3 are placed in the bottom of the chest: No. 1 against the left hand; No. 2 in the middle.

No. 4 is placed on top of Nos. 1 and 2, against the left end and the back of the chest; the division for the oil can on the left hand.

No. 5 is placed on top of Nos. 1, 2 and 3, against the front of the chest.

The shoeing box is placed on No. 3, against the right end and the back of the chest.

The tools and stores in all the boxes, and in the forges and battery wagons, are securely packed with tow.

Contents of Forge Body A.

TOOLS AND STORES.	No.	Weight.	PLACE.
		Lbs.	
Square iron, ½ in. and ⅝ in. - -	–	100.00	
Flat iron, 1¼ in.x⅝ in., 1 in.x½ in., and 1½ in.x¼ in. - - - -	–	50.00	In the iron room. The bars not more than 3 feet long; the square iron in 2 bundles.
Round iron, ⅜ in. - - -	–	50.00	
Cast steel, ⅝ in. square, - -	–	5.00	
English blister steel, - -	–	5.00	
Box A 6, containing: -	–	8 25	
Horseshoes, - - -	100	108.25	In the iron room.
Water bucket, wood, - -	1	10.00	On its hook.
Anvil, - - - -	1	100.00	On the fire place.
Vise, - - - -	1	29.00	Fixed on the stock of the carriage.
Water bucket. leather, - -	1	8.00	On the vise.
Bituminous coal, - -	–	250.00	In the coal box.
Coal shovel, - - -	1	4.75	
Padlock, - - - -	1	0.50	On coal box.
Tow, - - - -	–	2.00	
Total, exclusive of vise, -	–	693.50	

To put the box in the iron room or take it out, loosen the thumb nuts and raise the rear of the bellows an inch.

EQUIPMENT OF A BATTERY WAGON FOR A FIELD BATTERY.

The battery wagon for a field battery is designated by the letter C.

Limber Chest.

The chest is marked on the front side BATTERY WAGON C.

The tools and stores are carried in 4 *boxes* and 1 *oil can*.

The boxes are marked, respectively, C, Nos. 1, 2, 3 and 4.

Contents of Limber Chest for Battery Wagon C.

TOOLS AND STORES.	No.	Weight.	TOOLS AND STORES.	No.	Weight.
		Lbs.			Lbs.
Carriage Makers' Tools.			Box C 3, containing : -	-	12.5
Hand saws,) on inside of {	2	4.00	Felling axe,) with han- {	1	6.00
Tenon saw			Adze,) dles, {	1	3.30
(14-in.)) cover. {	1	1.50	Frame saw, -	1	4.50
Box C 1, containing : -	-	8 25	Quart can of sperm oil, -	1	2.70
Jack plane,	1	4.15	*Sadlers' Tools and Stores.*		
Smoothing plane, -	1	1.80			
Brace, with 24 bits,	1	4 35	Mallet, -	1	1.75
Spoke shave,	1	0 30	Clamp, -	1	5.00
Gauge,	1	0.30			23.25
Plane irons,	2	1.05			
Saw set, -	1	0 25	Box C 4, containing : -	-	11.00
Rule (2 feet),	1	0.14	Hammer, -	1	0.65
Gimlets, -	12	0.95	Shoe knife,	1	0 09
Compasses, pair,	1	0.18	Half round knife, -	1	0.28
Chalk line,	1	0.10	Shears, pair,	1	0.47
Brad awls,	2	0.15	Sandstone,	1	1.54
Scriber, -	1	0.15	Rule (2 feet),	1	0.14
Saw files (4½-in.), -	12	0 87	Needles, -	100	0.08
Wood files (10-in),	2	1.12	Awls and handles, -	12	0.75
Wood rasp (10 in).	1	0 40	Punches, -	2	0 22
Trying square (8-in.),	1	0 60	Pincers, pair,	1	0,75
Hand screw driver,	1	0 32	Pliers, pair,	1	0.22
		17 20	Claw tool, -	1	0 12
			Creaser, -	1	0.15
Box C 2, containing :	-	17.5	Thimbles, -	4	0,06
Oil stone,	1	1.50	Strap awl, -	1	0 01
Broad axe,	1	6 00	Beeswax, lbs.	2	2 00
Hand axe,	1	5.00	Black wax, lbs.	3	3 00
Claw hatchet,	1	2 00	Bristles, oz.	8	0 50
Claw hammer,	1	1 50	Shoe thread, lbs.	5	5 00
Pincers (small), pair,	1	1 06	Patent thread, lbs	2	2.00
Table vise, -	1	3 80	Buckles (assorted, .75-in.		
Framing chisels (1-in. and			to 1.5-in.), doz.	3	1.00
2-in.),	2	3.00	Tacks, M.	3	0 75
Firmer chisels (¾-in. and			Gunners' callipers, -	1	0.50
1½-in.),	2	1.00	Shoe knives, -	2	0 18
Framing gouges (1-in. and			Scissors, pairs,	2	0 20
1½-in.),	2	2.60			20 66
Augers and handles (½-in.,			Padlock, on the chest, -	1	0 50
⅝-in. and ¾ in.) -	3	2 35	Tar bucket, on its hook, -	1	7 00
Screw wrench, -	1	2 42	Tow, for packing, -	-	7.00
		32.23	Total, -	-	162 59

Boxes Nos. 1 and 2 occupy the bottom of the chest; No. 1 against the left end.

Nos. 3 and 4 are placed on top of Nos. 1 and 2; No. 3 against the rear of the chest.

Wagon Body C.

The large stores are piled loosely in the body and in the till; the small stores and tools are packed in *five boxes*.

The boxes are marked, respectively, C, Nos. 5, 6, 7, 8, and candle box C.

There are *seven* cans—*two* marked C, NEAT'S-FOOT OIL; *one* marked C, LINSEED OIL; *one* marked C, TURPENTINE; *two* marked C, OLIVE PAINT; *one* marked C, BLACK PAINT.

Contents of Wagon Body C.

TOOLS AND STORES.	No.	Weight.	TOOLS AND STORES.	No.	Weight.
		Lbs.			Lbs.
Box C 5, containing in 5 cans: - - -	–	17.5	Claw hatchet, ⎫ in axe	⎧ 1	2.
Linseed oil, gal.	1	9.17	Hand bills, ⎬ rack,	⎨ 2	4.
Spirits turpentine, gal.	1	8.77			
Olive paint, lbs.	50	56.			
Black paint, lbs.	5	6.5	Box C 6, containing: -	–	17.5
			Paint brushes, - -	12	3 00
Total in box C 5,	–	80.44	Sperm or wax candles, lbs.	5	7 85
			Rammer heads, -	4	2.90
Box C 7, containing in 2			Sponge heads, -	4	3.20
cans and 2 kegs: -	–	28.	Sponges, - -	12	3.00
Neat's foot oil, gals.	4	32.80	Priming wires, -	3	0.24
Grease, lbs.	50	60.	Gunners' gimlets, -	3	0.24
			Lanyards for friction pri-		
		92.80	mers, -	4	0.40
			Cannon spikes, -	6	0.30
Box C 8, containing: -	–	6.	Dark lanterns, -	3	3.00
Nails (4, 6, 8 and 10 pen-			Common lanterns, -	4	4.60
ny), lbs.	20	20.			
Felling axes in axe rack, -	2	12.	Total in box C 6, -	–	28.73

Contents of Wagon Body C.—Continued.

TOOLS AND STORES.		No.	Weight.	REMARKS.
			Lbs.	
Caisson stock,	- - -	1	35.	Under the till, against the side and rear of the wagon.
Splinter bar,	- -	1	15.	
Rammers and sponges,	- -	3	13.5	On the caisson stock, against rear end.
Spokes,	- - -	40	72.	On the bottom; piled lengthwise against the front end.
Fellies,	- - -	24	160.	On the spokes, crosswise.
Grindstone, 14-in. x 4-in.	-	1	50.	} On the fellies, against the left side of the wagon.
Arbor and crank for do.	-	1	6.5	
Screw jacks,	- -	3	75.	On the fellies, against the front and the till.
Wheel traces,	- -	10	47.5	⎫
Leading traces,	- -	10	57.5	⎪ In a pile occupying 30 inches at the
Collars,	- - -	6	27.5	⎪ rear end of the wagon, between
Girths,	- - -	16	11.	⎬ the left side and the caisson stock,
Whips,	- - -	16	8.	⎪ and up to the top of the till; the
Bridles,	- - -	6	18.	⎪ collars piled on each other, from
Halters,	- - -	6	21.	⎭ the bottom.
Halter chains,	- -	12	15.5	
Hame straps,	- -	25	4.5	
Spare nose bags,	- -	12	13.5	} On the harness.
Sash cord,	pieces,	6	10.	
Slow match,	yards,	2	0.25	On box No. 7, to the left of No. 8.
Elevating screw,	-	1	15.75	} On the pile of harness.
Pole yoke,	-	1	12.25	
Harness leather,	side,	1	25.	} Under the till, in front of the pile of harness, against the caisson stock.
Bridle leather,	sides,	2	22.	
Prolonge,	-	1	12.5	On box No. 7, in front of No. 8.
Scythes,	- -	4	9.	In the till, against the front end.
Scythe stones,	- -	4	6.	In the curve of the scythes.
Spades,	- -	6	30.	In the till; the bits against rear end.
Pick axes and handles,	-	2	13.	Between the spade handles.
Corn sacks,	-	24	20.	On the scythes.
Tarpaulins, 5 feet square,	-	2	18.	On the corn sacks, against front end.
Reaping hooks,	- -	4	3.85	Fastened to the ridge pole with a wooden clamp and a leather strap.
Scythe snaths,	-	4	12.	Fastened to the ridge pole with two leather straps and buckles.
Spare stock for battery wagon,		1	90.	In the spare stock stirrup.
Padlock,	-	1	0.5	
Watering bucket,	-	1	8.	Tied to the forage rack.
Forage,	- -	4	69.	In the forage rack.
Boxes,	- -	—	24.5	
Tow,	- -	—		
	Total,	—	1292.57	Exclusive of forage.

For *Equipment of the Forge for the Field-Park, and the Battery Wagon for the Field-Park*, see Ord. Manual, 2d edition, pp. 346–354.

FORGE FOR THE MOUNTAIN HOWITZER.

Two chests, designated the *forge chest* and the *smiths' tool chest*, contain the forge and the necessary tools for shoeing horses and making repairs.

The chests are carried on the sides of the pack-saddles, fastened by means of the lashing-chain.

The coal sack, containing the charcoal, is fastened to the arc by the handles.

Contents of the Forge Chest.

TOOLS AND STORES.	No.	Weight.	WHERE PLACED.
		Lbs.	
Fire place and frame, folded up,	1	31.5	On its side, the bottom against the back of the chest.
Bellows, closed, - - -	1	18.25	The right journal in the hole in the cleat on the bottom, the left in that in the clamp; the nozzle fastened to its support by the strap.
Bellows handle, - - -	1	1.875	On its cleat.
Wrench for nuts Nos. 1 and 4, -	1	1.0	In its bracket.
1 hand hammer with handle, -	1	2.375	Placed upright near the wrench.
1 riveting " " " -	1	1.5625	" " " " "
1 fore punch and creaser on same handle, - - - -	1	1.844	" " " " "
Bags of horse shoe nails, -	2	10.0	Packed with tow in the space to the right of the bellows.

Weight of forge chest, with cleats and clamps,   45. lbs.
   "   of tools and stores,   -   -   - 68.4 "
   "   of forge chest, packed, -   -   - 113.40 "

Contents of Smiths' Tool Chest.

TOOLS AND STORES.	No.	Weight	WHERE PLACED.
		Lbs.	
Anvil and block,	1	38.5	The head in the mortise of the rest, the block secured by the strap and buckle.
Water bucket (iron),	1	4.6875	On the moveable cleat resting on the anvil block.
Pair shoeing pincers,	1	1.875	In its cleat on the front with the vise.
Vise,	1	2.656	In its cleat.
Nailing hammer,	1	1.5	In brackets on front.
Shoeing "	1	.875	" " " "
Splitting chisel,	1	.8125	" " " "
Tongs, pair,	1	1.6875	In triangular cleat in the corner.
Pritchel,	1	.718	" " " " "
Hardie,	1	.406	In rack on the left end.
Clenching iron,	1	.9375	" " " "
Shoeing knife,	1	.406	In rack on the left end.
Poker,	1	.5	
Shovel,	1	.6875	In two wooden racks on the back of the chest.
Rake,	1	.531	
Nail punch,	1	.064	
Buttress,	1	1.469	On two hooks in the poker rack, held by a button.
Toe knife,	1	.50	In its cleats on the back of the chest.
Rasp,	1	1.5	In two racks on the back of chest, near the left end.
Square file,	1	.719	
Flat file,	1	1 031	In two cleats on the inside of cover, held by a button.
Half round,	1	.8125	
Bags horseshoe nails,	2	10.	One on the bottom at the left end, the other in the bucket.

Weight of the chest with cleats and racks, 44. lbs.
" " tools and stores, 72 875 "
" " chest packed, 116 875 "

Carriage Makers' Tools and Stores.

The tools and stores for the use of carriage makers, in repairing the carriages and equipments, are packed in two chests, which are like those for the ammunition, but without the interior divisions.

The two classes are designated by the letters A and B.

Contents of Carriage Makers' Tool Chests.

Chest A.	No.	Weight.	Chest A.	No.	Weight.
		Lbs.			Lbs.
Claw hatchet, - -	1	2.125	Wood files, 12-inch, -	2	1.125
Nailing hatchet, -	1	1.75	Sickles, - - -	2	2.125
Firmer chisels, ½ and ¾ in.	2	.594	Gunners' gimlet, - -	1	0.083
Trying square, - -	1	.422	Priming wire, - -	1	0.08
Bevel, - - -	1	.375	Gunners' pincers, -	1	1.25
Augers, ½ and ⅝ inch, and			Fuze cutter, -	1	
one handle, -	2	1.375	Papers of sprigs, 1 in. and		
Riveting hammer, - -	1	1.5	1½ in. - - -	2	1.0
Hand saw, - -	1	2.0	Papers of tacks, 8 oz. and		
Jack plane, - -	1	4.25	12 oz. - - -	2	1.25
Screw driver, - -	1	.375	Wood screws, ¾ in. No. 9,	60	0.31
Rule (two feet), - -	1	.156	Lbs. sash cord, - -	·2	2.0
Gimlets, - -	3	.1875	Lbs. twine, - -	½	.5
Hand saw files, - -	2	.125			

Weight of chest, - - . - - 21. lbs.
" of tools and stores, - - 24.96 "
" of chest packed, - - 46.96 "

Chest B.	No.	Weight	Chest B.	No.	Weight.
		Lbs.			Lbs.
Hand axe, - - -	1	3.25	Brad awls, - -	6	.5
Claw hatchet, - -	1	2.125	Sickles, - -	2	2.125
Nailing hatchet, -	1	1.75	Gunners' gimlet, - -	1	0.083
Firmer chisels, - -	2	0.594	Priming wire, - -	1	0.08
Firmer gouge, - -	1	0.25	Papers tacks, 8 & 12 oz. -	2	1.125
Pair compasses, -	1	0.25	Lb. twine, - -	½	0 5
Trying square, 6 inches, -	1	0.422	Leather thongs, -	25	0 344
Scriber, - -	1	0.125	Wood screws, 1½ and 1		
Riveting hammer, - -	1	1.5	inch, No 14, - -	36	0.562
Mallet, - -	1	2 25	Wood screws, 1½ and 2		
Gimlets, - -	3	0.1875	inch, No. 16, - -	12	0.312
Screw driver, - -	1	0.375	Nuts No. 1; 2, No. 2;		
Wood rasp, - -	1	0.5	6, No. 4, - -	12	0.625
Oil stone, - -	1	1.812	Washers No. 1, - -	12	0.437

Weight of chest, - - - 21. lbs.
" of tools, - - - 22.083 "
" of chest packed, - - 45. · "

The sickles are fastened to the front and back of the chests (inside) by small cleats at the necks and points. The other articles are securely packed in tow, the edges of the cutting tools being carefully wrapped up, to prevent injury.

Weights of Gun Carriages and Caissons, Equipped for Field Service.

DESIGNATION.	FOR GUNS.		FOR HOWITZERS.		
	6-pdr.	12-pdr.	12-pdr.	24-pdr.	32-pdr.
GUN CARRIAGE.	Lbs.	Lbs.	Lbs.	Lbs.	Lbs.
Gun, - - - -	884	1757	788	1318	1890
Gun carriage, without wheels, -	540	783	540	736	783
Two wheels, - - -	360	392	360	392	392
Limber body, without wheels, -	335	335	335	335	335
Two wheels, - - -	360	360	360	360	360
Ammunition chest, with interior divisions, - - -	185	182	206	198	192
Ammunition, packed, - -	395	497	465	541	470
Large tarpaulin, - -	36	36	36	36	36
Other implements and equipments, -	83	86	83	86	86
Total weight, -	3178	4428	3173	4002	4544
Number of rounds of ammunition on each limber, - -	50	32	39	23	15
CAISSON.	Lbs.	Lbs.	Lbs.	Lbs.	Lbs.
Body, without wheels, - -	432	432	432	432	432
Two wheels, - - -	360	360	360	360	360
Two ammunition chests, -	370	364	412	396	384
Ammunition, packed in do. -	790	994	930	1082	940
Limber body, without wheels, -	335	335	335	335	335
Two wheels, - - -	360	360	360	360	360
Ammunition chest, - -	185	182	206	198	192
Ammunition, packed in do. -	395	497	465	541	470
Large tarpaulin, - -	36	36	36	36	36
Other implements and spare parts, -	246	246	246	246	246
Total weight, -	3509	3806	3782	3986	3755
Number of rounds of ammunition on each caisson and its limber, -	150	96	117	69	45

Weights of Forges and Battery Wagons equipped for Field Service.

DESIGNATION.	For the Battery.	For the Park.
FORGE.	Lbs.	Lbs.
Body complete, without wheels, - • • • •	997	997
Two wheels, - • • • • •	360	360
Anvil and water buckets, • • • •	118	118
Stores in iron room, • • • • •	320	455
Stores in coal box, • • • • •	255	255
Limber body, without wheels, • • •	335	335
Two wheels, • · • • •	360	360
Limber chest, empty, - • • • •	158	158
Stores and tools on the limber, • - •	480	332
Total weight, -	3383	3570
BATTERY WAGONS.	Lbs.	Lbs.
Body complete, without wheels, • • • •	910	910
Two wheels, • • • • •	360	360
Stores in wagon body, • • • •	1289	2583
Limber body, without wheels, • • •	335	335
Two wheels, • • • • •	360	360
Limber chest, empty, • • • •	158	158
Stores and tools on the limber, • • •	162	200
Total weight (exclusive of forage), -	3574	4915

FIELD TRAIN.

Ordnance.

The proportion of artillery to other troops varies generally between the limits of 1 and 3 pieces to 1,000 men, according to the force of the army, the character of the troops of which it is composed, the force and character of the enemy, the nature of the country which is to be the theatre of war, and the character and objects of the war.

Similar considerations must regulate the selection of the kinds of ordnance and the proportions of the different kinds in the train.

The following principles may be observed in ordinary cases:

2 pieces to 1,000 men.
$\begin{cases} \frac{2}{3} \text{ guns, of which} \\ \frac{1}{3} \text{ howitz's, of which} \end{cases}$
$\begin{cases} \frac{1}{4} \text{ are 12-pdrs.} \\ \frac{3}{4} \text{ `` } \text{ 6-pdrs.} \\ \frac{1}{4} \text{ `` } \text{ 24-pdrs. or 32-pdrs.} \\ \frac{3}{4} \text{ `` } \text{ 12-pdrs.} \end{cases}$

Distributed as follows:

For the infantry.—1 piece to 1,000 men; 6-pdr. guns and 12-pdr. howitzers, in batteries of foot artillery.

For the cavalry.—2 pieces to 1,000 men; 6-pdr. guns and 12-pdr. howitzers, in batteries of horse artillery.

For the special and general parks of reserve:

1 piece to 1,000 men.
$\begin{cases} \frac{1}{2} \text{ in 12-pdr. batteries} \\ \frac{1}{3} \text{ `` } \text{ 6-pdr. } \text{ ``} \end{cases}$ of foot artillery.
1-6 in 6-pdr. batteries of horse artillery.

Ammunition for Cannon.

200 rounds to each piece, both of the reserves and of the active batteries.

The ammunition which cannot be carried in the caissons attached to the pieces will be kept in boxes with the reserves.

Additional supplies of ordnance and ordnance stores are placed in convenient depots, according to circumstances.

Ammunition for Small Arms.

100 rounds to each man; of which, for the musket, 40 rounds are in the cartridge box, 60 in the parks of reserve. In the same proportion for other small arms.

Percussion caps in the proportion of 12 caps to 10 cartridges.

Composition of a Battery on the War Establishment.

KIND OF BATTERY.					12-pdr.	6-pdr.
GUNS.	{ 12-pounders, mounted,	·	·	·	4	
	{ 6-pounders, "	·	·	·	–	4
HOWITZERS.	{ 24-pounders, "	·	·	·	2	
	{ 12-pounders, "	·	·	·	–	2
	Total number of pieces,			·	6	6
CAISSONS.	{ for guns,	·	·	·	8	4
	{ for howitzers, ·		·	·	4	2
					12	6
TRAVELLING FORGE,	·	·	·		1	1
BATTERY WAGON,	·	·	·	·	1	1
	Whole number of carriages with a battery,			·	20	14
AMMUNITION.	For 4 guns.	{ Shot, ·	·	·	448	400
		{ Spherical case,	·	·	358	320
		{ Canisters,	·	·	90	80
					896	800
	For 2 howitzers.	{ Shells,	·	·	168	120
		{ Spherical case,	·	·	112	160
		{ Canisters,	·	·	42	32
					322	312
	Total number of rounds with a battery,			·	1,218	1,112
DRAUGHT HORSES.	{ 6 to each carriage, ·	·		·	120	84
	{ Spare horses, one-twelfth,	·		·	10	7
			Total,	·	130	91

NOTE.—For two 32-pdr. howitzer carriages and 4 caissons, { Shells, · — 112
the number of rounds of ammunition is · · { Spherical case, 84
{ Canisters, · 14

Total, 210

HARNESS, corresponding to the number of horses to the carriages.

Battery of Mountain Howitzers.

Howitzers, - - - -	6
Gun carriages, - - - -	7
Ammunition chests, - - -	36 (48 rounds for ea. howitzer.)
Forge and tools, in two chests, - -	1
Set of carriage makers' tools, in 2 chests,	1
Pack saddles and harness, -	33
Horses or mules, - -	33

Such additional supplies of the above kinds as may be thought necessary will be carried with the park of reserve, together with the necessary ammunition for infantry, in packs.

A mountain howitzer ammunition chest will carry about 700 musket ball cartridges.

Rocket Battery.

No regular organization of a rocket battery has been arranged.

The nature and number of rockets, and of carriages or conductors, will be determined by the character of the service for which they may be required.

The Field Park.

The spare carriages, reserved supplies of ammunition, tools and materials for extensive repairs, and for making up ammunition, for the service of an army in the field, form the *field park*, to which should be attached also the batteries of reserve.

The quantities of these supplies must depend in a great measure on the particular circumstances of the campaign.

The ammunition required for artillery and small arms (according to the proportions above stated), in addition to what can be carried by the batteries and the troops, will be carried with the park, in caissons, or in store wagons.

For *Ordnance for Siege Train*, see Ord. Manual, 2d edition, p. 364–368.

For *Armament of Fortifications*, see Ord. Manual, 2d edition, p. 369–373.

CHAP. IX.

MECHANICAL MANŒUVRES AND ARTILLERY PRACTICE.

A board of officers has been recently charged with revising and arranging the manœuvres of heavy ordnance; some general directions with regard to the mechanical manœuvres are retained here for present use.

FIELD ARTILLERY.

The manœuvres may be performed by the men attached to the piece, and require no other implements than those belonging to the piece.

Begin, in all cases, by unlimbering and taking off the implements attached to the carriage.

To change a Wheel.

Tighten the cap squares; raise the elevating screw to its whole height; raise the carriage by means of two handspikes, one in the bore of the piece, and the other crossed under the first; support the carriage whilst the wheel is changed. For the 12-pdr. carriage, dig a hole 6 in. deep under the wheel that is to remain, in order to prevent it from sliding.

To dismount a Piece.

Take off the cap-squares; run up the elevating screw to its whole height; raise the trail; stand the piece upon its muzzle on the ground, and withdraw the carriage.

To mount a Piece.

Put a handspike under the piece a little in rear of the rimbases, and another under the cascable; place 2 men at the first handspike, 4 at the second, and 2 at the handles, or (if the piece has no handles) 4 at each handspike, and raise the piece upon its muzzle; bring up the carriage, raise the trail, and put the piece in its place; put on the cap squares, and lower the trail, relieving the weight of the piece by raising the muzzle.

In this manœuvre and the preceding, it may be necessary, with the 12-pdr. and larger calibres, to make a hole in the ground for the mu zle.

When a piece is upset, separate it from its carriage and remount it as above.

To transport a Piece by means of the Limber.

Detach the prolonge; place the limber over the piece so that the pintle hook shall be over the handles (or over the rear of the trunnions), with the breech toward the pole; raise the pole, and elevate the muzzle of the piece; lash the piece to the pintle hook, with the prolonge, by passing the ring of the prolonge twice through the handles (or round the piece in rear of the trunnions), and over the pintle hook; with the loose end of the prolonge lash the cascable to the fork of the limber.

Or, the gun may be placed on blocks at the proper height, and then lashed to the limber as before.

Siege Artillery.

To change a Piece from the Trunnion Holes to the Travelling Position.

Required : 11 men—6 handspikes—1 gun roller—1 small half roller—1 purchase block—2 gun chocks—4 roller chocks—6 wheel chocks—1 trace rope.

The carriage must be limbered up, or the trail raised upon 3 blocks and a half block.

Chock the wheels, depress the muzzle; remove the elevating screw, and place a roller under the reinforce.

Lift the muzzle, pushing the piece back, hauling at the same time on the trace rope attached to the knob of the cascable, until the trunnions come over their position. Remove the roller, and lower the breech on the bolster.

To change a Piece from its Travelling Position to the Trunnion Holes.

The carriage being limbered up, or the trail resting on 4 blocks and 1 half block.

Place a roller under the reinforce as near as possible to the rimbases.

Raise the chase, and let the gun run forward to its position, checking it with the trace rope attached to the knob of the cascable. As soon as the trunnions pass over the chin bolts, depress the muzzle, and the trunnions drop into their holes.

Remove the roller and put in the elevating screw.

For *Mechanical Manœuvres* of all classes of guns and howitzers, see Ord. Manual, 2d ed., chap. XII, and Manual of Heavy Artillery.

ARTILLERY PRACTICE.

The plan of this work does not include the details relative to the service of artillery; but, in the absence of more full and accurate tables of firing, it is thought useful to give here the mean results of such trials of the ranges of our ordnance as have been made from time to time by the ordnance department, together with some other practical information derived from authentic sources:

DRIFT OF RIFLE PROJECTILES.

Experiments show that *elongated* balls, when fired from an arm that is *rifled*, deviate to the right or left, according as the projectile is made by the grooves to revolve to the right or left. The deviation is always in the direction of the revolution of the projectile. In nearly all arms the twist of the grooves causes the projectile to revolve to the *right*.

In the *Enfield rifle* this *drift* is about 10 feet in 870 yards.

The following table gives the *drift* at different distances, for the French rifle (model 1842) with a twist of 4.37 feet, and a bullet with a single groove:

Distance in yds.	218	328	437	546	656	765	874	984	1093	1312	1421
Drift in ft. & in.	.5″	1′.1″	1′.9″	2′.0″	4′.9″	7′.6″	11′ 6″	16′.1″	21′.0″	38′.4″	50′.6″

The mean *drift* of 40 shots fired from two rifle muskets (C. S. model), at a distance of 1,150 yards in a perfectly calm day, was about 18 feet; not a single shot deviated to the left.

Cause of drift.—This irregular deviation results from the combined action of the *two* rotary motions to which the projectile is subject; the motion of rotation around its axis caused by the grooves of the rifle, and the slight *tendency to rotate* around an axis perpendicular to the first.

This last *tendency to rotate* is caused by the fact, that as the projectile moves, it does not always retain its axis tangential to the trajectory, and in this inclined position the resultant of the *resistances of the air passes above* the centre of gravity of the projectile, thus producing a slight rotation of the point of the projectile upwards. The effect of these two motions of rotation is to turn the point to the right, and thus produce the deviation observed. The forces thus acting upon the projectile are similar to those which act upon the well known philosophical instrument called the *gyroscope.*

It is probably possible to remove the cause of *drift,* by constructing the projectile so that the *resultant of the resistances of the air shall pass through its centre of gravity.*

DEVIATIONS OF THE SMOOTH-BORED CANNON.

These deviations, which no accuracy of aim can overcome, are due to two causes: (1), windage; (2), the *eccentricity* of the centre of gravity of the ball or shell. The deviation is generally the resultant of the two causes. Experiments made in France have demonstrated that the deviation arising from these two causes, though not always, is generally an elevation. The average deviation amounted to 3½ minutes in guns and 10½ minutes in howitzers, one-fourth of the shot from the guns having an elevation of more than $8\frac{1}{2}$ minutes, or a depression below the axis of $1\frac{1}{2}$ minute. In howitzers one-fourth had an elevation of more than $15\frac{1}{2}$ minutes, and one-fourth $5\frac{1}{2}$ minutes above the axis, the remaining shots passing within these limits. In a horizontal direction half of the shots deviated from the axis more than $4\frac{1}{2}$ minutes to the right or left.

In 1850, experiments in France with 8 and 12-pounders, gave the following results against a target 30 x 3 *metres*, representing a troop of cavalry :

Distance in metres,	•	•	•	•	500	600	700	800	900
Per ct. of 12-pdr. hits,	•	•	•	•	64	54	43	37	32
Per ct. of 8-pdr. hits,	•	•	•	•	67	44	40	28	28

This table shows the superiority of a 12-pdr. over a 6-pdr. for all distances over 550 yards.

BREACHING WITH RIFLE CANNON.

The breaching power of rifle cannon is much greater than that of the ordinary smooth bored siege cannon. This has been shown by an experiment lately made in England with Armstrong guns throwing projectiles of 40, 80 and 100 lbs. weight.

The subject of this experiment was a tower 30 feet high and 48 feet diameter. The walls were from 7 feet 3 inches to 10 feet thick, of solid brick masonry of good quality. The distance was 1,032 yards, more than twenty times the usual breaching distance.

The 80 pound shot passed completely through the masonry (7 feet 3 inches), and the 40 pound shot and 100 pound percussion shells lodged in the brick work, at a depth of five feet. After firing 170 projectiles, a small portion of which were loaded shells, the entire land side of the tower was thrown down.

The superior breaching power of rifle projectiles depends not only on penetration, but on great accuracy of flight, whereby they can be quickly concentrated on any desired point.

BREECH SIGHTS.

To determine the height of the breech sight for different angles of elevation.—First measure carefully the circumference of the swell of the muzzle and divide it by 3.1416. The quotient will be the exterior diameter of the muzzle. In the same manner determine the diameter of the base ring. *Half* the difference between these diameters will be the *dispart* of the gun. This determines the height of the muzzle sight required to make the line of sight parallel to the axis of the bore.

Now measure carefully the exact length of the gun from the *swell of the muzzle*, or centre of the muzzle sight, to the rear of the *base ring*. This distance multiplied by the *natural tangent* of 1°, 2°, 3°, &c. (taken from the table of tangents) will give the height of the breech sight, necessary to elevate the gun 1°, 2°, 3°, &c. When there is no *muzzle sight the dispart* must be subtracted from the height of the *breech sight* thus calculated.

Breech sights, in an emergency, may be made, in the field, of pasteboard or thin wood, to answer a very good purpose.

Ranges.

The range of a shot or shell is the first graze of the ball on horizontal ground, the piece being mounted on its appropriate carriage.

The range of a spherical case shot is the distance at which the shot bursts near the ground, in the time given; thus showing the elevation and the length of fuze required for certain distances.

Kind of Ordnance.	Powder.	Ball.	Elevation.	Range.	Remarks.
	Lbs.		°	Yds.	
6-*pdr. field gun.*	1.25	Shot.	0	318	
		"	1	674	
		"	2	867	
		"	3	1138	
		"	4	1256	
		"	5	1523	
	1.25	Sph. case	1 0	600	Time, 2 seconds.
		shot.	1 45	700	" 2¾ "
		"	2 0	800	" 3 "
		"	2 45	900	" 3½ "
		"	3 0	1000	" 3¾ "
		"	3 15	1100	" 4 "
		"	4	1200	" 5 "
12-*pdr. field gun,* model 1841.	2.5	Shot.	0	347	
		"	1	662	
		"	1 30	785	

Ranges—Continued.

KIND OF ORDNANCE.	Powder	Ball	Elevation.	Range.	REMARKS.
	Lbs.		°	Yds.	
12-*pdr. field gun*, model 1841. Continued.	2.5	Shot.	2	909	
		"	3	1269	
		"	4	1455	
		"	5	1663	
	2.5	Sph. case	1	600	Time, 1¾ seconds.
		"	1 45	700	" 2½ "
		"	2	800	" 2¾ "
		"	2 15	900	" 3 "
		"	2 30	1000	" 3¼ "
		"	3	1100	" 4 "
		"	3 30	1200	" 4½ "
12-*pdr. field gun*, Napoleon.	2.5	Shot.	0	325	
		"	1	620	
		"	2	875	
		"	3	1200	
		"	4	1320	
		"	5	1680	
	2.5	Sph. case	0 30	300	Time, 1 second.
		shot.	1 0	575	" 1¾ seconds.
		"	1 30	633	" 2½ "
		"	2 0	730	" 3 "
		"	3 0	960	" 4 "
		"	3 30	1080	" 4¾ "
		"	3 45	1135	" 5 "
	2.0	Shell.	0	300	" 0¾ "
		"	0 30	425	" 1¼ "
		"	1	616	" 1¾ "
		"	1 30	700	" 2¼ "
		"	2 0	787	" 2¾ "
		"	2 30	925	" 3½ "
		"	3 0	1080	" 4 "
		"	3 45	1300	" 5 "
12 *pdr. field howitzer.*	1.	Shell.	0	195	
		"	1	539	
		"	2	640	
		"	3	847	
		"	4	975	
		"	5	1072	
	0.75	Sph. case.	2 15	485	Time, 2 seconds.

Ranges—Continued.

KIND OF ORDNANCE.	Powder.	Ball.	Elevation.	Range.	REMARKS.
	Lbs.		° ′	Yds.	
12-*pdr. field howitzer.* Continued.	0.75	Sph. case. "	3 15 3 45	715 1050	Time, 3 seconds. " 4 "
12-*pdr. mountain howitzer.*	0.5	Shell. " " " " " "	0 1 2 2 30 3 4 5	170 300 392 500 637 785 1005	Time, 2 seconds. " 3 "
	0.5	Sph. case. " " " "	0 2 30 3 4 4 30	150 450 500 700 800	Time, 2 seconds. " 2½ " " 3 "
24-*pdr. field howitzer.*	2.	Shell. " " " "	0 1 2 3 4 5	295 516 793 976 1272 1322	
	2.5	Sph. case. " " " " " "	1 30 2 0 2 30 2 45 3 15 3 45 3 50	600 700 800 900 1000 1100 1200	Time, 2 seconds. " 2½ " " 3¼ " " 3½ " " 4 " " 4½ " " 4¾ "
32-*pdr. field howitzer.*	2.5	Shell. " " " " "	0 1 2 3 4 5	290 531 779 1029 1203 1504	
	3.25	Sph. case. " " " " " "	1 30 2 0 2 15 2 45 3 0 3 35 3 45	600 700 800 .900 1000 1100 1200	Time, 2 seconds. " 2½ " " 3 " " 3½ " " 3¾ " " 4½ " " 4¾ "

Ranges—Continued.

KIND OF ORDNANCE.	Powder.	Ball.	Elevation.	Range.	REMARKS.
	Lbs.		° ′	Yds.	
18-*pdr. siege and garrison gun.* On barbette carriage.	4.5	Shot. " " " "	1 2 3 4 5	641 950 1256 1450 1592	
24-*pdr. siege and garrison gun.* On siege carriage.	6.	Shot. " " " " " "	0 1 1 30 2 3 4 5	412 842 953 1147 1417 1666 1901	
32-*pdr. sea coast gun.* On barbette carriage.	6. 8.	Shot. " " " " " " "	1 45 1 1 30 1 35 2 3 4 5	900 713 800 900 1100 1433 1684 1922	
42-*pdr. sea coast gun.* On barbette carriage.	10.5	Shot. " " " "	1 2 3 4 5	775 1010 1300 1600 1955	
8-*inch siege howitzer.* On siege carriage.	4.	Shell, 45 lbs. " " " " "	0 1 2 3 4 5 12 30	251 435 618 720 992 1241 2280	
8-*inch sea coast howitzer.* On barbette carriage.	4. 6.	Shell, 45 lbs. " " " " " "	1 2 3 4 5 1 2	405 652 875 1110 1300 572 828	

Ranges—Continued.

KIND OF ORDNANCE.	Powder.	Ball.	Elevation.	Range.	REMARKS.
	Lbs.		° ′	Yds.	
8-*inch sea coast howitzer.* On barbette carriage. Continued.	6.	Shell, 45 lbs.	3	947	
		"	4	1168	
		"	5	1463	
	8.	"	1	646	
		"	2	909	
		"	3	1190	
		"	4	1532	
		"	5	1800	
10-*inch sea coast howitzer.* On barbette carriage.	12.	Shell, 90 lbs.	1	580	
		"	2	891	Time, 3 seconds.
		"	3	1185	" 4 "
		"	3 30	1300	
		"	4	1426	" 5¼ "
		"	5	1650	" 6 "
8-*inch columbiad.**	10.	Shell, 50 lbs.	1	681	Time, 1.88 seconds.
		"	2	1108	" 3.58 "
		"	3	1400	" 4.30 "
		"	4	1649	" 5.41 "
		"	5	1733	" 6.25 "
		"	6	1994	" 7.56 "
		"	7	2061	" 7.96 "
		"	8	2250	" 9.12 "
		"	9	2454	" 10.16 "
		"	10	2664	" 10.91 "
		"	11	2718	" 11.3 "
		"	12	2908	" 13. "
		"	13	3060	" 14.08 "
		"	14	3123	" 14.25 "
		"	15	3138	" 16. "
		"	20	3330	" 18.40 "
		"	25	3474	" 20. "
		"	30	3873	" 25. "
		Shot.	5	1697	" 6.20 "
		"	15	3224	" 14.19 "
10-*inch columbiad.**	15.	Shell, 100 lbs.	3	1068	Time, 3.20 seconds.
		"	5	1525	" 5.64 "
		"	8	2238	" 8.10 "
		"	10	2720	" 10.98 "
		"	12	2847	" 11.73 "
		"	20	3842	" 18.92 "

* Axis of gun 6 feet above the horizontal plane.

Ranges—Continued.

KIND OF ORDNANCE.	Powder.	Ball	Elevation.	Range.	REMARKS.
	Lbs.	Shell,	° ′	Yds.	
10-*in. columbiad*—Contin'd.	15.	100 lbs.	30	4836	Time, 27.50 seconds.
		Shot,	15	3281	" 14.32 "
		125 lbs.	30	5163	" 27.08 "
	18.	"	0	394	Axis of gun 16 feet
		"	1	752	above the water.
		"	2	1002	
		"	3	1230	
		"	4	1570	
		"	5	1814	
		"	6	2037	Shot ceased to rico-
		·"	8	2519	chet on water.
		"	10	2777	
		"	15	3525	
		"	20	4020	
		"	25	4304	
		"	30	4761	
		"	35	5433	
	20.	"	39 15	5654	
	12.	Shell,	1	800	
		100 lbs.	2	1012	
		"	3	1184	
		"	4	1443	
		"	5	1604	
	18.	"	0	448	
		"	1	747	
		"	2	1100	
		"	3	1239	
		"	4	1611	
		"	5	1865	
		"	6	2209	
		"	8	2489	
		"	10	2848	
		"	15	3200	
		"	20	3885	
		"	25	4150	
		"	30	4651	
		"	35	4828	Time of flight, 35 s.
15-*in. columbiad.*	40.	·Shell,	0	273	
		302 lbs.	1	484	
		"	2	812	
		"	3	1136	
		"	4	1310	
		"	5	1518	
		"	6	1760	
		"	7	1948	
		315 lbs.	8	2194	

Ranges—Continued.

KIND OF ORDNANCE.	Powder.	Ball.	Elevation.	Range.	REMARKS.
	Lbs.	Shell.	°	Yds.	
15-*in. columbiad*—Contin'd.	40.	315 lbs.	9	2236	Time, 8 87 seconds.
		"	10	2425	" 10 00 "
		"	12	2831	" 12 07 "
		"	15	3078	" 13 72 "
		"	20	3838	" 17 82 "
		"	25	4528	" 22 03 "
		"	28	4821	" 24 18 "
		"	30	5018	" 26.71 "
	45.	"	25	4595	" 23 20 "
	50.	"	25	4680	" 23.29 "
13-*in. sea coast mortar.*	20.	Shell. 200 lbs.	45	4325	
10-*in. sea coast mortar.*	10.	Shell. 98 lbs.	45	4250	Time, 36 seconds.
10-*in. siege mortar.*	1.	Shell, 90 lbs.	45	300	Time, 6 5 seconds.
	1.5		45	700	" 12 "
	2.	"	45	1000	" 14 "
	2.5	"	45	1300	" 16 "
	3.	"	45	1600	" 18 "
	3 5	"	45	1800	" 19 "
	4.	"	45	2100	" 21 "
	Lb oz				
8-*in. siege mortar.*	0 10	Shell, 46 lbs.	45	500	Time, 10 seconds.
	13	"	45	600	" 11 "
	1	"	45	750	" 12½ "
	1 2	"	45	900	" 13 "
	1 3	"	45	100 0	" 13½ "
	1 4	"	45	1100	" 14 "
	1 6	"	45	1200	" 14½ "
24-*pdr. coehorn mortar.*	Oz.		°	Yds.	
	0.5	Shell, 17 lbs.	45	25	
	1.	"	45	68	
	1.5	"	45	104	
	1.75	"	45	143	
	2.	"	45	165	
	2 75	"	45	260	
	4.	"	45	422	
	6.	"	45	900	
	8.	"	45	1200	

Service Projecting and Bursting Charges for Rifle Shells used in the C. S. Army.

SHELLS.

1862.	7-inch Rifle.	7.44 Blakely.	6.40 Rifle (Columbiad).	6.40 Rifle (32-pdr).	5.82 Rifle (Columbiad).	4.2-10 Parrott, 30-pdr.*	4.62 Siege Rifle.	10-pd. Parrott.*	3-inch Rifle.	2.25 Mountain Rifle.	3.80 James Rifle.*	12-pd. Blakely.	5.3-10 Rifle, 18-pdr.	20-pd. Parrott.*	2.50 Steel Rifle.	Whitworth B. Loading.	Dahlgren Brass Rifle.*	4-pd. State Rifle.	12-pd. State Rifle.
	Lbs	Lbs	Lbs	Lbs	Lbs.	Lbs	Lbs	Lbs	Lbs	Lbs	Lbs	Lbs	Lbs	Lbs	Lbs	Lbs	Lbs	Lbs	Lbs
Service bursting charge,	2.5	2.75	2.	1.5	1.75	1.5	1.43	.43	.37	1.75	.34	.12	1.	.75	.12	.31	s. shot	.43	.75
Service projecting charge,	12.	12.	11.	7.	8.	3.5	4.	1.	1.	.43	1.5	1.25	4.	2.	.5	1.75	.5	1.	1.25

* Those marked with an asterisk are captured guns. The "State rifles" are Virginia pieces, cast iron, rifled and banded.

Elevation, Ranges, and Times of Flight of 10-pdr. Parrott Gun.

ELEVATION.		TIME.	RANGE.	REMARKS.
Deg.	Min.	Seconds.	Yards.	
0	00	$\frac{1}{2}$	300	With long muzzle sight giving line of sight
1		1	450	parallel to axis, aim direct up to 300
2		2	900	yards.
3		3	1300	
4		$4\frac{1}{2}$	1600	
4	30	5	1760	
5		6	1950	
5	30	$6\frac{1}{4}$	2200	
6		7	2300	
7		$8\frac{1}{4}$	2600	
10		$10\frac{1}{2}$	3000	
12		$12\frac{1}{4}$	3600	
15		16	4100	
20		$19\frac{1}{4}$	5000	
25		$23\frac{1}{2}$	5600	
30		$27\frac{1}{2}$	5900	
35		$31\frac{1}{2}$	6200	

The range of 3-inch rifle gun, with 7, or 11, or 13 grooves, does not vary materially from this, up to 2,300 yards—6° elevation giving 2,250 yards.

Height of Breech Sight for Different Angles of Elevation.

Degrees.	Bronze Guns and Howitzers, Model of 1841. Height of Hausse, in inches.							Iron Guns and Howitzers, Models of 1839, 1841, and 1844. Height of Hausse, in inches.			
	Guns.			Howitzers.				Siege and Garrison.			
								Guns.		Howitzers.	
	12-pdr.	12-pdr. Napoleon.	6-pdr.	32-pdr.	24-pdr.	12-pdr.	Mountain 12 pdr.	24-pdr.	18-pdr.	8-in.	24-pdr.
0.0	−1.331	−2.500	−1.025	−1.300	−1.125	−.922	−.349	−2.907	−2.938	−.900	−1.050
0.30	−.666	−1.933	−.512	−.652	−.565	−.461	−.063	−1.938	−1.966	−.451	−.511
1.0	0.001	−1.365	0.000	.004	.006	.022	.224	−.969	−.992	.001	.029
1.30	0.668	−.798	0.512	.657	.572	.484	.511	0.000	−.018	.449	.568
2.0	1.334	−.230	1.025	1.310	1.138	.946	.799	.969	.957	.898	1.108
2.30	2.001	.338	1.538	1.963	1.704	1.407	1.087	1.939	1.933	1.348	1.648
3.0	2.668	.907	2.051	2.617	2.271	1.870	1.375	2.910	2.909	1.799	2.189
3.30	3.336	1.476	2.565	3.272	2.838	2.332	1.663	3.882	3.886	2.250	2.730
4.0	4.005	2.045	3.077	3.927	3.406	2.795	1.951	4.885	4.864	2.701	3.271
4.30	4.675	2.616	3.594	4.583	3.974	3.259	2.240	5.829	5.843	3.153	3.814
5.0	5.345	3.187	4.110	5.239	4.544	3.724	2.529	6.804	6.824	3.606	4.357
5.30	6.017	3.759	4.627	5.897	5.114	4.189	2.819	7.781	7.806	4.059	4.901
6.0	6.689	4.332	5.144	6.556	5.686	4.655	3.109	8.760	8.790	4.513	5.445
6.30	7.363	4.906	5.663	7.216	6.258	5.121	3.399	9.740	9.775	4.968	5.991
7.0	8.038	5.481	6.182	7.878	6.831	5.589	3.691	10.722	10.763	5.423	6.538
7.30	8.715	6.057	6.703	8.541	7.406	6.058	3.983	11.706	11.752	5.880	7.086
8.0	9.393	6.635	7.224	9.205	7.982	6.527	4.275	12.693	12.744	6.338	7.635
8.30	10.073	7.214	7.747	9.871	8.559	6.998	4.568	13.682	13.739	6.797	8.186
9.00	10.754	7.795	8.272	10.539	9.138	7.471	4.862	14.674	14.736	7.257	8.738

To estimate Distances, approximately.

Height of breech sight for the different angles under which an object 6½ feet high is seen, at the distance of

KIND OF GUN.	200 Yards.	300 Yards.	400 Yards.	500 Yards.	600 Yards.	700 Yards.	800 Yards.	900 Yards.	1000 Yards.	1100 Yards.	1200 Yards.
	In.	In.	In.	In.	In.	In.	In.	In.	In.	In.	In.
GUNS. Field, 6-pdr.	.636	.424	.318	.254	.212	.182	.159	.141	.127	.116	.106
Field, 12-pdr.	.827	.551	.413	.331	.276	.236	.207	.184	.165	.150	.138
Siege, 18-pdr.	1.209	.806	.604	.484	.403	.345	.302	.269	.242	.219	.201
Siege, 24-pdr.	1.202	.801	.601	.481	.401	.344	.300	.267	.240	.218	.200
Garrison, 32-pdr.	1.213	.809	.607	.485	.404	.346	.303	.269	.242	.220	.202
Garrison, 42-pdr.	1.246	.831	.624	.493	.415	.356	.312	.277	.249	.226	.208
Mountain, 12-pdr.	.356	.238	.165	.143	.120	.102	.089	.079	.070	.065	.059
HOWITZERS. Field, 12-pdr.	.572	.382	.286	.229	.191	.164	.143	.127	.115	.104	.095
Field, 32-pdr.	.702	.468	.351	.280	.234	.201	.176	.156	.140	.127	.117
Siege, 24-pdr.	.809	.540	.405	.324	.270	.231	.202	.180	.162	.147	.135
Siege, 24-pdr.	.671	.446	.335	.268	.223	.191	.166	.149	.134	.122	.112
Siege, 8-inch.	.558	.372	.279	.223	.186	.159	.139	.124	.112	.102	.093

To use the foregoing table, aim over the line of metal, first at the top of an object 6½ feet high,—for instance, the cap of a foot soldier; then aim at his feet, by using a breech sight, without moving the gun. The distance found in the preceding table corresponding to this height of breech sight will be the distance of the object from the gun.

Initial Velocities of Cannon Balls.

The initial velocity of a *cannon ball* is about 1,500 feet per second. It varies from 1,400 feet to 1,800 feet, depending on the weight of the charge and the strength of the powder. The initial velocity of *shells* and *spherical case* is less, varying from 1,050 to 1,400, the charge of powder being less.

Initial Velocities of Balls fired from Small Arms.

KIND OF ARMS.	Charge.	Weight of ball.	Initial velocity.	
	Grains.	Grains.	Feet.	
Rifle musket, - -	60	510	963	Elongated ball.
Rifle, 1855, - -	60	510	914	"
Altered musket, - -	70	740	879	"
Pistol carbine (U. S.), -	40	468	603	"
Musket, 1841, - -	110	412	1500	Round ball.

Loss of the Velocity by the Windage of the Ball.

The loss of velocity by a windage of 1-40 diameter varies from 8 to 12 per ct. The loss is directly as the windage and inversely as the bore.

For *Penetration of Shot and Shells in Masonry, Brick, &c.*, see Ord. Manual, 2d ed., p. 396–401.

Penetration in Fascines, Wool, &c.

At the distance of 24 yards, a musket round ball penetrates 20 inches into a gabion stuffed with sap fagots; the ball from a wall piece, 23.63 inches. The resistance of fascines decreases very rapidly by the twigs being broken or separated by the balls.

A *rolling gabion*, stuffed with fascines, is proof against the ball of a wall piece at 15 yards; at the distance of 200 yards, and even more, it is pierced through by cannon balls of the smallest calibre.

The penetration of balls in wool is more than double that in compact earth, even when the wool is contained in close, well quilted mattresses pressed between hurdles. At 40 yards, a musket ball (round) penetrates more than 40 inches into woollen mattresses thus placed together.

It has been ascertained by experiment that a musket round ball, having a velocity of 362 feet, at the moment of impact, will just pass through a white pine board 1 inch thick; and that, with the same velocity, the ball has sufficient force to shatter the leg bone of an ox covered with one thickness of stout harness leather. A musket ball moving with this velocity would, therefore, inflict a wound which would disable a man or beast; or a spherical case shot having this velocity at the moment of bursting would be effective against troops in its immediate vicinity.

A musket ball with an initial velocity of 583 feet will pass through one inch white pine board at 100 yards : hence a spherical case shot, moving with that velocity at the moment of bursting, would be effective at 100 yards distant from the place of bursting. The remaining velocity at 100 yards as computed, is 394 feet.

Penetration of Small Arms in White Pine seasoned.

KIND OF ARM.	WEIGHT OF CHARGE.		Diameter of Ball.	PENETRATION.			
	Ball.	Powder.		30 yds.	200 yds.	600 yds.	1000 yds.
	Grs.	Grs.	In.	In.	In.	In.	In.
Rifle musket, - - -	500	–	.5775	–	11.	6.33	3.25
Altered musket, - - -	730	60	.685	–	10.5	6.33	3.5
Harper's Ferry rifle, - -	500	70	.5775	–	9.33	5.66	3.0
Pistol carbine, - - -	450	40	.5775	–	5.75	3.0*	
Sharp's carbine, - - -	463	60	.55	7.27			
Burnside's " - - -	350	55	.55	6.15			

* At 500 yards.

CHAP. X.

MISCELLANEOUS INFORMATION.

RECOIL OF GUN.

The recoil of a gun depends on its weight, the amount of powder used and the weight of the projectile. In a light gun the recoil is considerable. It is very great in the old 12-pdr. carronades. When the axis of the trunnions is below the axis of the piece, the effect of the reaction of the gas against the breech is to increase the pressure of the trail against the ground, and thereby diminish the distance of recoil. When the axis of the trunnions is above the axis of the bore, the effect is to diminish the pressure on the trail when the gun is fired; and hence the distance of recoil is augmented. In the C. S. service the axis of the trunnions is in the exact plane of the axis of the bore.

EFFECT OF PREVENTING RECOIL.

When the powder is changed into gas, by its explosive force, it projects the ball forward and the gun backward, and thus increases the space occupied by the gas. If the gun is checked in its backward movement by preventing the recoil, this space is by so much diminished, and the force to burst the gun consequently increased.

Hence, there is always danger of bursting heavy siege guns, when fired at *large angles of elevation*, as thereby the recoil is diminished, the pressure of the gun on the carriage being more nearly vertical. At the siege of Sevastopol the bursting of the siege guns was attributed to their being fired with too great elevation.

ENDURANCE OF GUNS.

Iron guns have been known to bear from 1,500 to 3,000 rounds with service charges, and only require the vent to be *rebouched*. At the siege of Sevastopol many heavy guns endured over 3,000 rounds. Experience has shown that the length of time that a piece has been cast, has a very great influence upon its endurance. Two 8-inch columbiads of same form and dimensions, and cast in the same way, were tried. One of them had been cast only a few days, and the other six years previous. The one tested a few days after casting, failed at the 72d round. The other sustained 2,582 rounds without yielding.

This apparent anomaly is explained by the fact, that iron, like other substances, possesses the property of accommodating itself to a new and unnatural position, and of finally becoming stronger in this position than in the original one. A new arrangement takes place among the crystals, in accordance with the solicitation of external forces.

INFLUENCE OF EXTERIOR MOULDINGS ON THE STRENGTH OF GUNS.

As a general rule, cast iron guns burst through the vent, that being a weak point for the action of the powder. From thence the line of fracture passes along the axis to the front of the trunnions, where it turns off to the right or left, or both, leaving the rest of the chase entire. The rule is universal, that the planes of fracture follow the track, with considerable precision, of all *re-entering angles* on the exterior of the gun. This is not without cause. It is a law of physics, that crystals arrange and group themselves with their principal axes in lines perpendicular to the cooling or heating surfaces of the solid. A simple illustration of this law is seen in ice *rotten* from the heat it has absorbed from the air and water. The crystals are all found to be arranged vertically, and are easily pushed through. This form of crystallization takes place in iron, cast to form a gun, and *planes of weakness* occur just where the crystals, perpendicular to the different surfaces, join confusedly together, giving less cohesion to the metal than at any other part.

These *planes of weakness* are in a measure avoided now, by avoiding all unnecessary mouldings and sudden changes of plane on the exterior of the gun.

BURSTING OF RIFLE CANNON.

When a rifle cannon is fired, the windage by which a portion of the gas escapes, is cut off by the sudden forcing of the soft metal at the base of the projectile, into the grooves of the rifle. The gas, thus momentarily confined, possesses more tension than in a smooth bore; and hence a greater power to burst the cannon. This difficulty is obviated by making rifle cannon very heavy in the breech, or better, by reinforcing the breech with a heavy wrought iron band, as in the Parrott guns. Too much care cannot be used in sending the projectile home against the charge in rifle cannon. If sufficient space intervenes between the projectile and the powder, the whole of the powder is converted into gas of powerful tension, before the projectile moves—that is, before its inertia is overcome. The consequence is, that being thus suddenly checked, it reacts, and exerts a powerful strain upon the gun.

The bursting of some of the large rifle cannon in the C. S. service, is supposed to be due to the stripping off part of the soft metal from the base of the projectile, and thus wedging it fast in the bore. Accidents of this character are now avoided by attaching to the base of the ball a copper saucer, which destroys windage, and imparts to it, by taking the grooves, the desired rotary motion.

PRESSURE OF GUNPOWDER PER SQUARE INCH.

[From Capt. Rodman's Experiments.]

The pressure on a 42-pounder gun, at the bottom of the bore, when fired with 10 lbs. of powder and a solid shot weighing 43 pounds, is 44,535 pounds.

8 lbs. of powder, of a grain .1 inch diameter, with the same gun and shot, gave a pressure of 51,800 lbs.

8 lbs. of powder, of a grain .4 inch diameter, with the same gun and shot, gave a pressure of 31,900 lbs.

12.67 lbs. of powder, of a grain .6 inch diameter, and a solid shot weighing 186.3 lbs., fired from a 11 inch gun, gave a pressure of 21,370 lbs.

The same weight of .3 in. diameter, gave a pressure of 35,330 lbs.

The same weight of .3 inch diameter, of different powder, gave a pressure of 65,920 lbs.

Half the weight of powder of the ordinary charge, with double the weight of shot, gave the same pressure as the ordinary charge.

1 lb. of powder, burned in a space equal to twice that occupied by the powder, gave a pressure of 42,500 lbs.

2 lbs. burned in the space occupied by it, gave a pressure of 133,590 lbs.

1 lb. burned in the space occupied by it, .1 inch grain, gave a pressure of 185,000 lbs.

The actual pressures are probably greater than those above given.

RESISTANCE OF THE AIR.

When a ball is projected from a cannon it is acted on by three forces : (1.) the impulsive force ; (2.) the force of gravity ; (3.) the resistance of the air. Were the last named force entirely destroyed, the trajectory of the ball would be a portion of a parabola : but owing to its existence, the path of the ball is never a true parabola, but considerably deflected from it, especially in the latter part of the branch.

The experiments of Robins established that the resistance of air for very great velocities, increased in a far greater ratio than that of the square of the velocity. He determined that the resistance of air on the surface of a bullet, three-fourths of an inch in diameter, with a velocity of 1,650 feet, amounted to a pressure of ten pounds. By the application of mathematics to the experiments of Robins, the following pressures are computed to arise from the resistance of the air. These are necessarily modified slightly by the condition of the air.

A	6-pdr. ball,	with a velocity of 1,650 feet, meets with a resistance of						234 lbs.
A	12-pdr. ball,	"	"	" "	"	"	.	360 "
A	24-pdr. ball,	"	"	" "	"	"	.	624 "
A	32-pdr. ball,	"	"	" "	"	"	.	736 "
A	42-pdr. ball,	"	"	" "	"	"	.	882 "
A	64-pdr. ball,	"	"	" "	"	"	.	1,152 "
An	130-pdr. ball,	"	"	" "	"	"	.	1,950 "

Influence of shape of ball.—A spherical ball meets with less resistance than one that is flattened, and a conical˒pointed ball less than a sphere of same diameter.

A *paraboloid* meets with less resistance than any other surface. This form causes the greatest divergence of the deflected currents, and consequently meets with the least opposition from the resistance of the air. It results, therefore, that cylindro-conical balls have a more flattened trajectory, and a greater dangerous space.

CAUSES OF DIFFERENCE IN THE ENDURANCE OF CANNON WHEN CAST SOLID AND WHEN CAST HOLLOW.

All field pieces and ordinary columbiads in use are cast solid, and afterwards bored out to the proper calibre. When cast solid, the cooling, and consequent contraction of the metal begins on the exterior and proceeds inwards. The exterior is thus placed under a force of compression, while a force of elongation acts upon the interior. The more rapid the cooling, the greater will be this strain to burst the gun, beginning at the interior. It is an established law, that the strain produced on any material by the action of a central force, diminishes as the square of the distance from the centre increases. Now, when a central force, as exploded powder, is applied to a gun thus strained, the interior being under a force of elongation, and the exterior under one of compression, it develops, in a gun, one calibre in thickness, *nine times* the strain on the interior that it does on the exterior, *independent of previous strain;* so that there exists the permanent strain arising from difference of contraction, *added* to that produced by the central force, to break the interior.

In all ordinary guns, it is found that this difference of contraction does not injure the gun so much as to prevent it from being serviceable for 1,000 or 1,500 rounds—and the guns are cast solid because the method is cheaper and simpler. This permanent strain arising from difference of contraction, would be so great in very large guns, as to seriously injure them, and prevent their use were they cast solid—consequently the 15-inch columbiads are cast *hollow*, and cooled from the *interior*, by allowing water to flow through a pipe passed through the centre of the core, and at the same time keeping the exterior heated. The consequence is, that contraction begins on the interior and proceeds outward, producing a force of compression in the interior, and one of extension in the exterior, thus *reversing the strain*, acting in opposition to that produced by the action of the powder. Capt. Rodman, of the U. S. service, was the first to successfully apply this method.

It will be seen, from the following table, that the endurance of guns, cast hollow, greatly surpassed those cast solid, in every case, where both were cast in pairs, at the same time and from the same material.

Date.	DESCRIPTION.	ROUNDS FIRED.	
		Cast solid.	Cast hollow.
1849	First pair, 8-inch, - - -	85	251
1851	Second pair, 8-inch, - - -	73	1500
1851	Third pair, 10-inch, - - -	20	249
	Total number of fires, -	178	2000

WEIGHTS AND MEASURES.

Measures of Length.

Inches.	Feet.	Yards.	Rods or Poles.	Furlongs.	Mile.
12	1				
36	3	1			
198	16½	5½	1		
7920	660	220	40	1	
63360	5280	1760	320	8	1

The inch was formerly divided into three parts, called *barleycorns,* and also into 12 parts called *lines,* neither of which denominations is now in common use. Scales and measuring rules are generally divided into *inches*, *quarters*, *eighths*, and *sixteenths;* or into *inches* and *decimal parts;* the latter of these divisions is used in the Ordnance Department.

For surveying land : 7.92 inches = 1 link. } Gunter's
  100 links = 4 poles, or 22 yards, or 66 feet. } chain.

For map making : Chains are often made of 50 links, each 1 foot in length.

For measuring ropes and soundings : 1 fathom = 6 feet.
  1 cable's length = 120 fathoms.

For measuring cloth : 1 nail = 2¼ inches = 1-16th of a yard.
  1 quarter = 4 nails.
  1 yard = 4 quarters.
  1 ell English = 5 quarters.

For measuring horses : 1 hand = 4 inches.

Geographical measure : 1 degree of a great circle of the earth = 69.77 miles.
  1 geographical or nautical mile = 1-60th of a degree of the earth = 2025 yards.
  1 nautical league = 3 miles.

New French system.—The basis of the new French system of measures is the measure of a meridian of the earth, a quadrant of which is 10,000,000 *metres*, measured at the temperature of 32° Fahr.   The multiples and divisions of it are decimal, viz :
1 metre = 10 decimetres = 100 centimetres = 1,000 millimetres = 39.3707971 English inches, or 3.2809 feet.

Road measure.—Myriametre = 10,000 metres.   Kilometre = 1,000 metres.   Decametre = 10 metres.   Metre = 0.51317 toise.

According to Capt. Kater's comparison, 1 metre = 39.37079 English inches.

Measures of Surface.

Square measure. 144 square inches = 1 square foot.
  9 square feet = 1 square yard.

Land measure. 30¼ square yards = 1 square perch or pole.
  40 perches = 1 rood.
  160 perches = 4 roods = 1 acre = 10 square chains.   (Gunter's)
    = 4,840 square yards = 70 yards square nearly.
  640 acres = 1 square mile.

Measures of Solidity.

Cubic or solid measure. 1 cubic foot = 1,728 cubic inches.
  1 cubic yard = 466.56 cubic inches = 27 cubic feet.

Measuring stone. In different parts of the United States the *perch* of stone denotes a different quantity, but it is usually 24¾ cubic feet.

Measuring wood. 1 cord is a prism 4 ft. square and 8 ft. long = 128 cubic feet.

Measures of Capacity.

Liquid Measure.

Gills.	Pints.	Quarts.	Gallon.
4	1		
8	2	1	
32	8	4	1

The standard gallon of the United States is the old wine gallon, which measures 231 cubic inches, and contains (as determined by Mr. Hassler), 58373 troy grains, or 8.3388822 avoirdupois pounds, of distilled water at the maximum density (39°.83 Fahr.); the barometer being at 30 inches.

A cubic foot contains 7.48 gallons.

A box 6 x 6 x 6.42 inches contains 1 gallon.

A box 4 x 4 x 3.61 inches contains 1 quart.

Dry Measure.

Pints.	Quarts.	Gallons.	Pecks.	Bushel.
2	1			
8	4	1		
16	8	2	1	
64	32	8	4	1

The standard bushel of the United States is the Winchester bushel, which measures 2150.4 cubic inches, and contains 543391.89 troy grains, or 77.627413 lbs. avoirdupois, of distilled water, under the circumstances above stated.

A cubic yard contains 21.69 bushels.

A cylinder 14 in. diam. x 14 in. deep } contains 1 bushel.
Or a box 16 x 16.8 x 8 inches

A box 12 x 11.2 x 8 inches contains ½ bushel.

A box 8 x 8.4 x 8 inches contains 1 peck.

N. B.—It will be observed that the pint, quart and gallon of dry measure, are not the same as for liquid measure.

Measures of Weight.

Avoirdupois Weight.

Drams.	Ounces.	Pounds.	Quarters.	Cwt.	Ton.
16	1				
256	16	1			
7168	448	28	1		
28672	1792	112	4	1	
573440	35840	2240	80	20	1

The *standard avoirdupois pound* of the United States, as determined by Mr. Hassler, is the weight of 27.7015 cubic inches of distilled water weighed in air, at the temperature of the maximum density (39°.83); the barometer being at 30 inches.

Troy Weight.

Grains.	Dwt.	Ounce.	Pound.
24	1		
480	20	1	
5760	240	12	1

The pound, ounce and grain are the same in apothecaries' and troy weight; in the former, the ounce is divided into 8 drachms, the drachm into 3 scruples, and the scruple into 20 grains.

$$7000 \text{ troy grains} = 1 \text{ lb. avoirdupois.}$$
$$175 \text{ troy pounds} = 144 \text{ lbs. avoirdupois.}$$
$$175 \text{ troy ounces} = 192 \text{ oz. avoirdupois.}$$
$$437\tfrac{1}{2} \text{ troy grains} = 1 \text{ oz. avoirdupois.}$$

PHYSICAL DATA.

Working Power of Men and Horses.

Men.—A *foot soldier* travels in 1 minute,

In common time, 90 steps = 70 yards.
In quick time, 110 steps = 86 yards.
In double quick, 140 steps = 109 yards.

He occupies in the ranks a front of 20 inches, and a depth of 13 inches, without the knapsack; the interval between the ranks is 13 inches. 5 men can stand in a space of 1 square yard. Average weight of men, 150 lbs. each.

A *man* travels, without a load, on level ground, during 8½ hours a day, at the rate of 3.7 miles an hour, or 31¼ miles a day. He can carry 111 lbs., 11 miles in a day. A porter going short distances and returning unloaded, carries 135 lbs., 7 miles a day. He can carry in a wheelbarrow 150 lbs., 10 miles a day.

The maximum power of a strong man, exerted for 2½ minutes, may be stated at 18,000 lbs. raised 1 foot in a minute.

Mr. Field's experiments, 1838.

A man of ordinary strength exerts a force of 30 lbs. for 10 hours a day, with a velocity of 2½ feet in a second = 4,500 lbs. raised 1 foot in a minute = *one-fifth* the work of a horse.

Daily allowance of water for a man, 1 gallon, for all purposes.

Horses.—A *horse* travels the distance of 400 yards, at a walk, in 4½ minutes; at a trot, in 2 minutes; at a gallop, in 1 minute.

He occupies in the ranks a front of 40 in., a depth of 10 feet; in a stall, from 3½ to 4½ feet front; at picket, 3 feet by 9. Average weight of horses, 1,000 lbs. each.

A horse carrying a soldier and his equipments (say 225 lbs.), travels 25 miles in a day (8 hours).

A *pack horse* can carry 250 to 300 lbs., 20 miles a day.

A *draught horse* can draw 1,600 lbs. 23 miles a day; weight of carriage included.

Artillery horses should not be made to draw more than 700 lbs. each, the weight of the carriage included.

The ordinary work of a horse for 8 hours a day may be stated at 22,500 lbs. raised 1 foot in a minute.

In a horse mill, the horse moves at the rate of 3 feet in a second. The diameter of the path should not be less than 25 or 30 feet.

Daily allowance of water for a horse, 4 gallons.

Forage.—Hay, pressed in bundles: 11 lbs. to the cubic foot.

> Oats: 40 lbs. to the bushel, or 32.14 lbs. the cubic foot.

> Wheat: 60 lbs. to the bushel, or 48.21 lbs to the cubic foot.

A *horse power* in steam engines, is estimated at 33,000 lbs. raised 1 foot in a minute; but as a horse can exert that force but 6 hours a day, one steam horse power is equivalent to that of 4 horses.

The number of horse powers, in a single stroke engine, is expressed by $.0000238 \, d^2 \, n \, p \, l$; d being the diameter of the piston in inches, n the number of strokes in a minute, l the length of stroke in feet, and p the pressure of steam on a square inch (diminished usually by 1-5th for friction and inertia). In a double stroke engine the power is double the above.

Strength of Ice.

Ice 2 inches thick will bear infantry.

Ice 4 inches thick will bear cavalry or light guns.

Ice 6 inches thick will bear heavy field guns.

Ice 8 inches thick will bear 24-pdr. gun, on sledges; weight **not** more than 1,000 lbs. to a square foot.

Velocity of Sound.

At the temperature of 33° the mean velocity of sound is **1,100** feet in a second. It is increased or diminished *half a foot* for each degree of temperature above or below 33°.

Velocity and Force of the Wind.

VELOCITY.		Pressure on 1 square foot.	Common designations of the force of the winds.
In 1 hour.	In 1 second.		
Miles.	Feet.	Lbs.	
1	1.47	0.005	Hardly perceptible.
2	2.93	.020 }	Just perceptible.
3	4.40	.044 }	
4	5.87	.079 }	Gentle, pleasant wind.
5	7.33	.123 }	
10	14.67	.492 }	Pleasant, brisk breeze.
15	22.00	1.107 }	
20	29.34	1.968 }	Very brisk.
25	36.67	3.075 }	
30	44.01	4.429 }	High wind.
35	51.34	6.027 }	
40	58.68	7.873 }	Very high.
45	66.01	9.963 }	
50	73.35	12.300	A storm or tempest.
60	88.02	17.715	A great storm.
80	117.36	31.490	A hurricane.
100	146.70	49.200	A hurricane that tears up trees, carries buildings before it, etc.

Table of Natural Sines and Tangents.

DEG.	MIN.	SINE.	TANGENT.	DEG.	MIN.	SINE.	TANGENT.
0	10	0029089	0029089	12	30	2164396	2216947
	15	0043633	0043634		45	2206974	2262769
	30	0087265	0087269	13	00	2249511	2308682
	45	0130896	0130907		15	2292004	2354687
1	00	0174524	0174551		30	2334454	2400788
	15	0218149	0218201		45	2376859	2446984
	30	0261769	0261859	14	00	2419219	2493280
	45	0305385	0305528		15	2461533	2539676
2	00	0348995	0349208		30	2503800	2586176
	15	0392598	0392901		45	2546019	2632780
	30	0436194	0436609	15	00	2588190	2679492
	45	0479781	0480334		15	2630312	2726313
3	00	0523360	0524078		30	2672384	2773245
	15	0566928	0567841		45	2714404	2820292
	30	0610485	0611626	16	00	2756374	2867454
	45	0654031	0655435		15	2798290	2914734
4	00	0697565	0699268		30	2840153	2962135
	15	0741085	0743128		45	2881963	3009658
	30	0784591	0787017	17	00	2923717	3057307
	45	0828082	0830936		15	2965416	3105083
5	00	0871557	0874887		30	3007058	3152988
	15	0915016	0918871		45	3048643	3201025
	30	0958458	0962890	18	00	3090170	3249197
	45	1001881	1006947		15	3131638	3297505
6	00	1045285	1051042		30	3173047	3345953
	15	1088669	1095178		45	3214395	3394543
	30	1132032	1139356	19	00	3255682	3443276
	45	1175374	1183578		15	3296906	3492156
7	00	1218693	1227846		30	3338059	3541186
	15	1261990	1272161		45	3379167	3590367
	30	1305262	1316525	20	00	3420201	3639702
	45	1348509	1360940		15	3461171	3689195
8	00	1391731	1405408		30	3502074	3738847
	15	1434926	1449931		45	3542910	3788661
	30	1478094	1494510	21	00	3583679	3838640
	45	1521234	1539147		15	3624350	3888787
9	00	1564345	1583844		30	3665012	3939105
	15	1607426	1628603		45	3705574	3989595
	30	1650476	1673426	22	00	3746066	4040262
	45	1693495	1718314		15	3786486	4091108
10	00	1736482	1763270		30	3826834	4142136
	15	1779435	1808295		45	3867110	4193348
	30	1822355	1853390	23	00	3907311	4244748
	45	1865240	1898559		15	3947439	4296339
11	00	1908090	1943803		30	3987491	4348124
	15	1950903	1989124		45	4027467	4400105
	30	1993679	2034523	24	00	4067366	4452287
	45	2036418	2080003		15	4107189	4504672
12	00	2079117	2125566		30	4146932	4557263
	15	2121777	2171213		45	4186597	4610063

DEG.	MIN.	SINE.	TANGENT.	DEG.	MIN.	SINE.	TANGENT.
25	00	4226183	4663077	50	00	7660444	11917536
	30	4305111	4769755		30	7716246	12130970
26	00	4383711	4877326	51	00	7771460	12348972
	30	4461978	4985816		30	7826082	12571723
27	00	4539905	5095254	52	00	7880108	12799416
	30	4617486	5205671		30	7933533	13032254
28	00	4694716	5317094	53	00	7986355	13270448
	30	4771588	5429557		30	8038569	13514224
29	00	4848096	5543091	54	00	8090170	13763819
	30	4924236	5657728		30	8141155	14019483
30	00	5000000	5773503	55	00	8191520	14281480
	30	5075384	5890450		30	8241262	14550090
31	00	5150381	6008606	56	00	8290376	14825610
	30	5224986	6128008		30	8338858	15108352
32	00	5299193	6248694	57	00	8386706	15398650
	30	5372996	6370703		30	8433914	15696856
33	00	5446390	6494076	58	00	8480481	16003345
	30	5519370	6618856		30	8526402	16313517
34	00	5591929	6745085	59	00	8571673	16642795
	30	5664062	6872810		30	8616292	16976631
35	00	5735764	7002075	60	00	8660254	17320508
	30	5807030	7132931	61	00	8746197	18040478
36	00	5877853	7265425	62	00	8829476	18807265
	30	5948228	7399611	63	00	8910065	19626105
37	00	6018150	7535541	64	00	8987940	20503038
	30	6087614	7673270	65	00	9063078	21445069
38	00	6156615	7812856	66	00	9135455	22460368
	30	6225146	7954359	67	00	9205049	23558524
39	00	6293204	8097840	68	00	9271839	24750869
	30	6360782	8243364	69	00	9335804	26050891
40	00	6427876	8390996	70	00	9396926	27474774
	30	6494480	8540807	71	00	9455186	29042109
41	00	6560590	8692867	72	00	9510565	30776835
	30	6626200	8847253	73	00	9563048	32708526
42	00	6691306	9004040	74	00	9612617	34874144
	30	6755902	9163312	75	00	9659258	37320508
43	00	6819984	9325151	76	00	9702957	40107809
	30	6883546	9489646	77	00	9743701	43314759
44	00	6946584	9659888	78	00	9781476	47046301
	30	7009093	9826972	79	00	9816272	51445540
45	00	7071068	10000000	80	00	9848078	56712818
	30	7132504	10176074	81	00	9876883	63137515
46	00	7193398	10355303	82	00	9902681	71153697
	30	7253744	10537801	83	00	9925462	81443464
47	00	7313537	10723687	84	00	9945219	95143645
	30	7372773	10913085	85	00	9961947	114300520
48	00	7431448	11106125	86	00	9975641	143006660
	30	7489557	11302944	87	00	9986295	190811370
49	00	7547096	11503684	88	00	9993908	286362530
	30	7604060	11708496	89	00	9998477	572899620
				90	00	10000000	Infinite.

APPENDIX.

INSTRUCTIONS TO ORDNANCE OFFICERS IN THE FIELD.

The appointment of Brigade Ordnance Officers having been authorized, the following Instructions are substituted for those of May 20, 1862:

1st. The Chief of Ordnance of an army corps, and ordnance officers of separate commands, will correspond with the Chief of the Bureau of Ordnance relative to supplies of ordnance and ordnance stores, with the commands to which they are attached. Requisitions made, whether for money or stores, will be approved by the General commanding.

2d. The division ordnance officers will correspond with the Chief of Ordnance of the army corps to which the divisions are attached, and obtain supplies through him. They will be responsible for the property under their charge, and make weekly reports of ammunition on hand (consolidated from brigade reports) to this office.

3d. Brigade ordnance officers will, with the approval of the division ordnance officer, obtain one or more wagons for each regiment in their brigade, as ordnance wagons. These wagons will be separate from the train of wagons for reserve ammunition of the division, and will be marked with the name of the regiment to which they are assigned, and will be placed in charge of the Ordnance Sergeant of the regiment. The wagons will be covered, if possible, with painted cloth covers, for security against the weather, and each wagon will be supplied with a spare tarpaulin. These wagons will habitually follow their respective regiments.

4th. On the eve of battle the division ordnance officer will, under direction of the Chief of Ordnance of the army, station the ordnance wagons at the point selected for the division field depot of ammunition, under charge of the senior ordnance officer of brigades. He will keep himself acquainted with the movements of brigades, and cause the wagons of any brigade, which may be detached, to follow the movements of the brigade. Brigade ordnance officers will make weekly reports of ammunition on hand, to the division ordnance officers.

5th. The Ordnance Sergeants, together with the details habitually assigned to them from their regiments, will, under the direction of the brigade ordnance officers, constitute a corps devoted as well to the preservation of the captured and other ordnance stores, as to the supplies of ammunition of the various regiments. One man of each detail should follow the movements of the regiment, to ascertain its wants and communicate with the field depot. The habitual details from each regiment should be augmented before a battle, to not less than six men from each. The ammunition wagons, their loads temporarily removed, will, as circumstances favor, be employed to carry to the rear such arms and other captured stores as are left upon the battle field.

6th. Especial care must be taken in selecting competent, prompt and efficient men for the duties of Ordnance Sergeants. They may be removed for cause, and new appointments ordered, on the application of the division ordnance officers, through the Chief of Ordnance of the army corps, by the Commanding General.

7th. The ammunition wagons to each regiment will not supersede the necessity for division supply trains.

DUTIES OF ORDNANCE SERGEANTS.

1st. To obey the directions of the division ordnance officer, received through the brigade ordnance officer, or of the brigade ordnance officer (if the brigade is a separate command), in all relative to care and preservation of arms, and duties connected therewith.

2d. To take charge of all supplies, arms and ammunition of the regiment, and make returns of the same according to "Ordnance Regulations."

Issues to be made on written requisitions approved by the Colonel, or commanding officer of the regiment; which requisitions are to be filed with his "return of property."

3d. To take charge of the ordnance wagon or wagons attached to each regiment, and to see that it always contains at least 15 rounds per man of the regiment—surplus arms or accoutrements to be turned over to the brigade or division ordnance officer.

4th. To supervise the condition of the arms of the regiment, and get a detail of at least two mechanics to assist him in the necessary repairs to the arms; an account of these repairs to be kept, as far as possible, against each man of the regiment. Repairs to be made on the order of the Colonel of the regiment.

5th. To take charge of the arms and accoutrements of the sick of the regiment in hospitals, which will be kept until the sick are sent to the general hospital, when their arms will be turned over to the division depots, through the brigade ordnance officer.

6th. In battle, it will be the duty of the Ordnance Sergeants to remain with the ammunition wagons, and act with the details assigned to them from the regiments, under the orders of the ordnance officer, in supplying the troops with ammunition, collecting arms of the killed and wounded, and securing captured arms and ammunition.

J. GORGAS,
Col., Chf. of Ord.

Approved:

G. W. RANDOLPH,
Secretary of War.

July 1, 1862.

[No. 2.]

Relative to Returns of Ordnance Stores.

I. Returns for ordnance and ordnance stores issued to troops, will be made quarterly on the 31st March, 30th June, 30th September and 31st December, according to Form I, "Ordnance Regulations," as follows:

II. For all ordnance stores—such as arms, accoutrements, equipments and ammunition in the hands of a regiment or battalion, including the supplies carried in the ordnance wagon of the regiment—by the Colonel of the regiment, assisted by his Ordnance Sergeant.

III. For all ordnance stores—such as artillery harness, equipments, accoutrements and ammunition in the possession of field batteries—by the Captains of batteries.

IV. For ordnance and ordnance stores at posts or garrisons—by the Commanding Officer, assisted by his Ordnance Sergeant.

V. For ordnance stores in the division and army trains—by the Division Ordnance Officer and by the Assistant to the Chief of Ordnance of the army.

VI. Invoices to show what has been received, and receipts for issues, must accompany the "Returns," and the line of "Expenditures" must mention the actions or practice causing the expenditure; and where ammunition or stores are lost, proper evidence and explanation must be furnished, attached to the return.

VII. In many cases captains of infantry companies have given receipts for their arms and equipments. In such cases the Colonel of the regiment to which the company belongs, should give a receipt for the property in the possession of the company commander, at the organization of the regiment, making the necessary expenditures for property lost, worn out and expended on the regimental returns. Where property has been furnished by a State or by the company themselves, it will be accounted for on a separate return by the company commander, a remark to that effect being made in the regimental return.

VIII. Wherever there are field depots, with workmen attached, the usual monthly summary statement of work done, should be transmitted. (See Form 29, "Ordnance Regulations.")

J. GORGAS,
Col., Chief of Ordnance.

August 1, 1862.

Ordnance and Ordnance Stores.

The general denomination, "*Ordnance and Ordnance Stores,*" comprehends all cannon, howitzers, mortars, cannon balls, shot and shells, for the land service; all gun carriages, mortar beds, caissons and travelling forges, with their equipments; and all other apparatus and machines required for the service and manœuvres of artillery, in garrisons, at sieges, or in the field; together with the materials for their construction, preservation and repair. Also, all small arms, side arms and accoutrements, for the artillery, cavalry, infantry and riflemen; all ammunition for ordnance and small arms, and all stores of expenditure, for the service of the various arms; materials for the construction and repair of ordnance buildings; utensils and stores for laboratories, including standard weights, gauges and measures; and all other tools and utensils required for ordnance duty. The ordinary articles of camp equipage and pioneers' tools, such as axes, spades, shovels, mattocks, &c., are not embraced as ordnance supplies.

The ordnance department also for the present furnishes knapsacks, canteens and haversacks, which belong properly to camp equipage.

Rates of Prices of Guns, Carriages, &c.

Bronze guns and howitzers cost from 65 to 80 cents per pound. In peace they cost about 45 cents. Cast iron guns and howitzers cost from $7\frac{1}{2}$ to 9 cents per pound. In peace less. To *rifle a gun* costs from 20 to 30 dollars. Field carriages cost about $425. Field caissons cost about $450. In peace they cost much less.

The subjoined tables of rates refer to peace. At present the cost is considerably increased, in many instances doubled.

Rates of prices of Small Arms and Accoutrements.

PARTS.	PERCUSSION LOCK.		
	Musket.	Rifle.	Pistol.
	D. C.	D. C.	D. C.
Barrel with sight, without breech, - -	4 90	5 28	2 40
Breech screw, - - -	12	12	09
Bayonet or band stud, - - -	01		
Tang screw, - - -	06	06	05
Breech sight, - - -	–	07	
Cone, - - -	11	11	11
Lock plate, - - -	60	60	48
Tumbler, - - -	32	32	30
Tumbler screw, - - -	04	04	04
Bridle, - - -	19	19	17
Sear, ·. - -	24	24	20
Sear spring, - - -	12	12	10
Main spring, - - -	32	32	30
Lock screws, each, - - -	04	04	04
Hammer, - - -	72	72	54
Side plate (with band for pistol),	09	12	48
Side screws, each, - - -	05	05	04
Upper band, - - :	46	54	
Middle band, - - -	28		
Lower band, - - -	18	22	
Upper band spring, - - -	11	11	
Middle band spring, - - -	10		
Lower band spring, - - -	10	10	
Guard plate, - - -	50	60	42
Guard plate screws, each, - -	04	04	02
Guard bow without swivels, - -	36	42	24
Guard bow nut, each, - - -	02	02	02
Swivels and rivets, each, - -	12	12	
Trigger, - - -	14	14	11
Trigger screw, - - -	02	02	02
Butt plate, - - -	36	63	35
Butt plate screw, each, - -	03	03	03
Ramrod, - - -	60	60	30
Ramrod spring, - - -	14	14	
Ramrod wires, - - -	01	01	
Ramrod stop, - - -	01	01	
Stock, - - -	1 74	2 22	1 08
Bayonet, - - -	1 63		
Bayonet clasp, - - -	19		
Bayonet clasp screw, - - -	02		
Box plate, - - -	–	86	
Box catch, - - -	–	06	
Box spring, - - -	–	12	
Box spring screw, - - -	–	02	
Box screw, each, - - -	–	03	
Ramrod swivel and rivet,			30
Ramrod swivel and rivet screw, - -	–	–	02
Sword bayonet blade, - - -	–	2 00	
Sword bayonet hilt without clasp, - -	–	2 00	
Sight base, - - -	40		

Prices of Small Arms—Continued.

PARTS.				PERCUSSION LOCK.		
				Musket.	Rifle.	Pistol.
				D. C.	D. C.	
Long branch (leaf),	-	-	-	17		
Short,	-	-	-	24		
Sight screws, each,	-	-	-	03		
Sight complete,	-	-	-	1 00		
Barrel complete,	-	-	-	5 16	5 48	
Lock complete,	-	-	-	2 70	2 70	
Guard complete.	-	-	-	1 27	1 49	
Bayonet complete,	-	-	-	1 95		
Box plate complete,	-	-	-	–	1 16	
Arm complete,	-	-	-	15 60	15 90	
Appendages for all arms :						
Screw driver and cone wrench.						
Wiper.						
Ball screw.						
Spring vise.						
Bullet mould (rifle calibre).						

Swords and Sabres.

PARTS.		Cavalry Sabre.	Horse Artillery Sabre.	Artillery Sword.	Musketoon Sword Bayonet.	Non-commissioned Officer's Sword.	Musician's Sword.
		D. C.	D. C.	D. C.	D. C.	D. C.	D. C.
Hilt.	Gripe,	40	34	–	–	48	40
	Head,	1 40	88	1 74	3 20	1 00	88
	Guard,	2 20	1 16	–	–	2 40	88
Blade.		5 60	3 96	4 26	4 26	4 40	3 84
Scabbard.	Mouth piece,	40	20				
	Body,	2 40	2 00	1 00	1 24	1 32	1 00
	Bands and rings,	1 20	1 20				
	Ferule and stud,	30	26	50	80	70	50
	Tip,	–	–	50	50	70	50
Arm complete,		14 00	10 00	8 00	10 00	11 00	8 00

Accoutrements—(Black Leather Belts).

PARTS.	Infantry.	Artillery.	Cavalry.	Rifle.
	D. C.	D. C.	D. C.	D. C.
Cartridge box,	1 75	–	–	1 60
Cartridge box belt,	75			
Bayonet scabbard and frog,	75			
Waist belt (private's),	60	–	–	60
Cap pouch and pick,	65	–	65	65
Gun sling,	35	–	35	35
Sabre belt,	–	1 35	1 35	
Sword belt,	–	1 00		
Carbine or gun sling,	–	–	1 25	
Powder flask (tin),	30	–	30	30
Canteen,	25	25	25	25
Canteen strap,	20	20	25	25
Knapsacks,	3 25	3 25	3 25	3 25
Haversacks,	20	20	20	20

Ordnance Depots and Officers.

Col. J. Gorgas, - - -	Chief of Ordnance, -	Richmond, Va.
Maj. S. Stansbury, - - -	Arsenal, - -	Richmond, Va.
Capt. G. T. Getty, - - -	Ordnance Depot, -	Lynchburg, Va.
Lt. Col. J. A. d'Lagnel, - -	Arsenal and Armory,	Fayetteville, N. C.
Commanding officer, - - -	Ordnance Depot, -	Wilmington, N. C.
Commanding officer, - - -	Ordnance Depot, -	Knoxville, Tenn.
Maj. F. L. Childs, - - -	Arsenal, - -	Charleston, S. C.
Lt. Col. G. W. Rains, - -	Arsenal, - -	Augusta, Ga.
Maj. R. W. Cuyler, - - -	Arsenal, - -	Macon, Ga.
Commanding officer, - -	Ordnance Depot, -	Savannah, Ga.
F. C. Humphreys, M. S. K. -	Ordnance Depot, -	Columbus, Ga.
Capt. J. L. Henderson, - -	Ordnance Depot, -	Selma, Ala.
Commanding officer, - -	Ordnance Depot, -	Mobile, Ala.
C. G. Wagner, M. S. K. - -	Ordnance Depot, -	Montgomery, Ala.
M. Gayle, M. S. K. - - -	Arsenal, - -	Mt. Vernon, Ala.
Commanding officer, - -	Briarfield Arsenal, -	Columbus, Miss.

Dimensions of Small Arms Ammunition in the Photographic Supplement

	Weight (grains)	Diameter (inches)	Length (inches)
Plate 16. a.	519	.539	2.48
b.	597	.574	2.20
c.	471	.533	1.15
d.	496	.575	1.08
e.	850	.685	1.18
Plate 17. a.	603	.570	3.20
b.	636	.575	2.90
c.	900	.690	2.80
d.	530	.569	.99
e.	519	.568	1.00
f.	659	.665	.96
g.	828	.687	1.06
Plate 18. a.	561	.522	1.19
b.	497	.535	3.05
c.	423	.535	1.03
d.	387	.515	1.00
e.	297	.535	1.85
Plate 19. a.	385	.639	–
b.	474	.630	2.00
c.	543	.655	2.18
d.	618	.640	2.35
e.	728	.650	2.98
f.	577	.69	2.70
Plate 20. a.	383	.550	.86
b.	166	.390	1.91
c.	499	.520	1.83
d.	534	.545	2.21
e.	469	.537	1.08
f.	548	.548	2.15

Plate 21. a. 227	.453	1.27
b. 306	.580 (over case)	2.40
c. 147	.389	1.05
d. 167	.445 (over case)	1.65
e. 156	.380	1.47
f. 161	.384	1.55
g. 160	.390	1.38
Plate 22. a. 469	.577	.97
b. 451	.575	.95
c. 472	.562	1.01
d. 551	.570	2.48
e. 581	.58	2.21
f. 176	.412	1.00
g. 167	.407	.62
h. 802	.677	1.21

Plate 1.—Josiah Gorgas, Chief of Ordnance, C.S.A.

Plate 2.— ⓐ , James H. Burton, Superintendent of Armories; ⓑ , John W. Mallett, Superintendent of Laboratories.

Plate 3. — ⓐ , 12 lb. Napoleon gun; ⓑ , face of a 12 lb. Napoleon showing the marks of the Macon Arsenal.

a

b

Plate 4.— ⓐ , 12 lb. field howitzer; ⓑ , 3" Ordnance rifle.

a

b

Plate 5.— ⓐ , 10 lb. Parrott rifle; ⓑ , 20 lb. Parrott rifle.

Plate 6.—Whitworth breechloading rifle.

a

b

Plate 7.— ⓐ , 6 lb. field gun; ⓑ , 24 lb. field howitzer.

Plate 8.— ⓐ , 3" Armstrong shell; ⓑ , 12 lb. Whitworth shot; ⓒ , 6 lb. Blakeley (Britton) shot; ⓓ , 3" Archer shot.

Plate 9.— ⓐ , 3" Read shell; ⓑ , 3" Burton case-shot; ⓒ , 20 lb. Read shell; ⓓ , 20 lb. Read shell—a shorter variety than *c* , specimen exhibits severe base chipping.

Plate 10.— ⓐ , 6 lb. solid shot; ⓑ , 12 lb. case-shot (not to same scale as *c*); ⓒ , 12 lb. solid shot; ⓓ , 24 lb. solid shot.

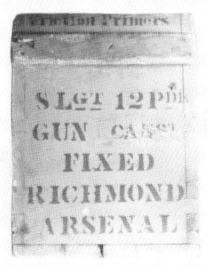

Plate 11.— (a) , 2.5" cannister; (b) , 12 lb. smoothbore cannister; (c) , Richmond Arsenal shipping crate for 12 lb. cannister.

Plate 12.— ⓐ , gunner's haversack; ⓑ , pendulum hausse for 12 lb. Napoleon; ⓒ , breech mount for *b;* ⓓ , thumbstall.

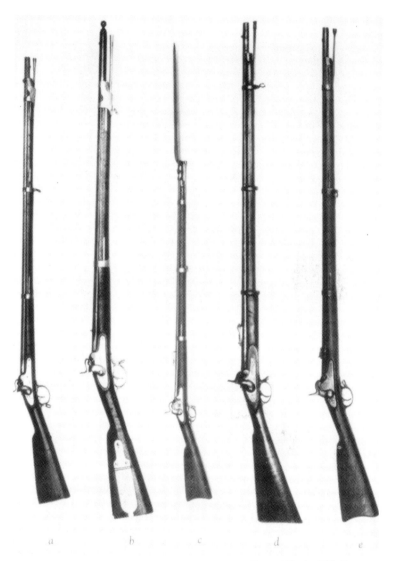

Plate 13.—MUZZLELOADING LONGARMS: ⓐ , .69 cal. Springfield, model 1842 smoothbore musket; ⓑ , .54 cal. Harpers Ferry, model 1841 "Mississippi" rifle; ⓒ , .58 cal. Springfield, model 1855 rifled musket; ⓓ , .577 cal. Enfield "Tower" rifled musket; ⓔ , .58 cal. Richmond rifled musket, 1861.

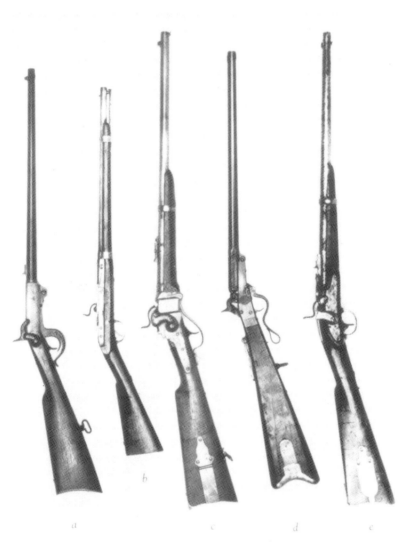

Courtesy Milwaukee Public Museum

Plate 14.—BREECHLOADING CARBINES: ⓐ , .54 cal. Burnside; ⓑ , .52 cal. Hall; ⓒ , 52. cal. Sharps, model 1859; ⓓ , .50 cal. Maynard, First Model; ⓔ , .54 cal. Merrill.

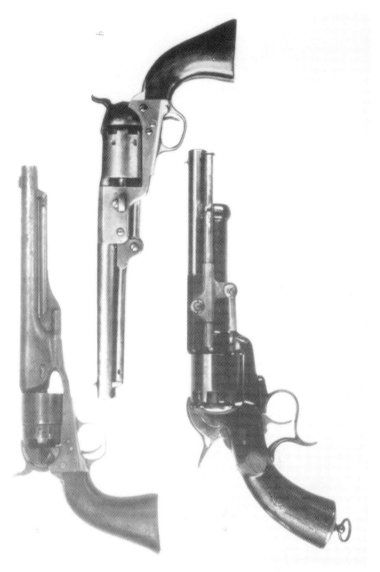

Plate 15.—REVOLVERS: ⓐ, .44 cal. Colt "Army," model 1860; ⓑ, .36 cal. Colt "Navy" type by Leech & Rigdon, C.S. 1862; ⓒ, LeMat "grapeshot," First Model, .41 cal. rifled barrel over .60 cal. smoothbore barrel.

Plate 16. — ⓐ , .54 cal. Gardner cartridge; ⓑ , .58 cal. Gardner cartridge; ⓒ , ball for *a*; ⓓ , ball for *b*; ⓔ , .69 cal. Gardner ball.

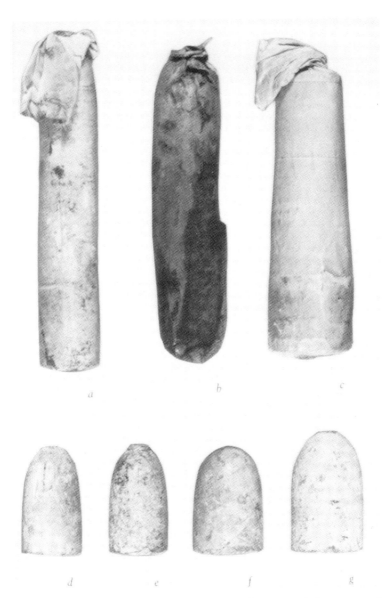

Plate 17.— ⓐ, C.S. mfg. .577 cal. Enfield cartridge; ⓑ, same, but ball is not reversed; ⓒ, .69 cal. English Tower cartridge; ⓓ, .577 cal. Enfield ball, side cast; ⓔ, same, nose cast; ⓕ, .69 cal. Tower ball; ⓖ, same, heavier pattern.

Plate 18. — ⓐ , .54 cal. rifled musket ball; ⓑ , same, cartridge by Macon Arsenal; ⓒ , .54 cal. rifled musket ball; ⓓ , same, variant; ⓔ , .54 cal. rifled musket cartridge, round ball.

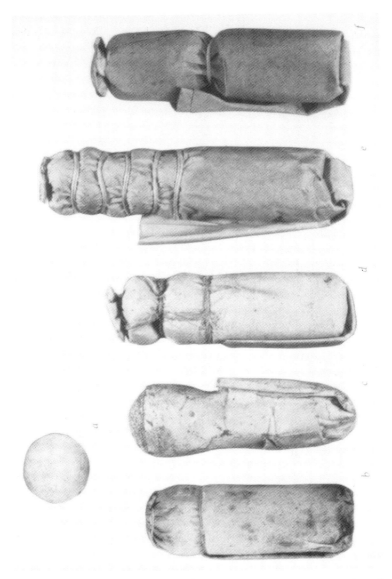

Plate 19.— ⓐ , .69 cal. round ball; ⓑ , .69 cal. round ball cartridge, Richmond Arsenal; ⓒ , same, Selma Arsenal; ⓓ , .69 cal. Buck & Ball cartridge, Richmond Arsenal; ⓔ , .69 cal. Buckshot cartridge; ⓕ , same, Columbus Ord. Depot.

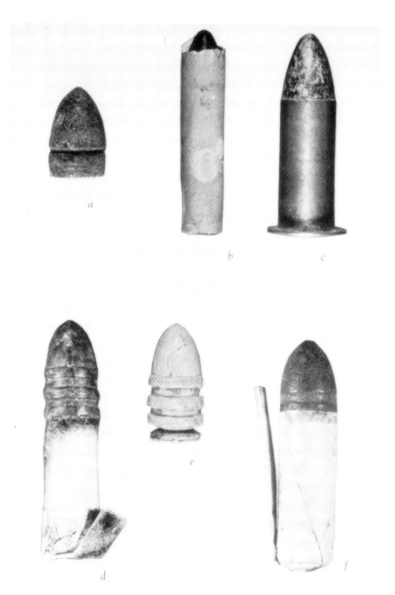

Plate 20.— ⓐ , .54 cal. Merrill carbine ball, Richmond Arsenal; ⓑ , .37 cal. Maynard rifle cartridge, Savannah Ord. Depot; ⓒ , .50 cal. Maynard rifle cartridge, northern manufacture; ⓓ , .52 cal. Sharps rifle cartridge, Richmond Arsenal; ⓔ , ball for d; ⓕ , .52 cal. Sharps carbine cartridge, Richmond Arsenal.

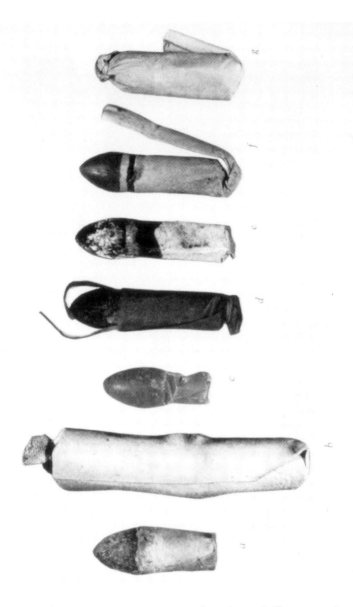

Plate 21. — ⓐ , .44 cal. Colt Army cartridge, Richmond Arsenal; ⓑ , same, combustible cartridge inside protective paper envelope; ⓒ , .36 cal. Colt Navy cartridge, Richmond Arsenal; ⓓ , same, Augusta Arsenal; ⓔ , same, fabricating facility unknown; ⓕ , same, fabricating facility unknown; ⓖ , same, Savannah Ord. Depot.

Plate 22.— ⓐ , .58 cal. rifled musket ball, nose cast; ⓑ , same, variant; ⓒ , same, Lynchburg Ord. Depot; ⓓ , same, cartridge, Lynchburg Ord. Depot; ⓔ , .60 cal. Buckshot cartridge for LeMat revolver, Richmond Arsenal; ⓕ , .41 cal. LeMat ball cartridge; ⓖ , ball for ƒ; ⓗ , .69 cal. rifled musket ball.

Plate 23.—Cartridge Packet Labels: ⓐ , .577 or .58 cal. rifled musket, Augusta Arsenal; ⓑ , same, Selma Arsenal; ⓒ , same, Macon Arsenal; ⓓ , .54 cal. rifled musket, Macon Arsenal; ⓔ , .69 cal. Buck & Ball, Richmond Arsenal.

Plate 24.—CARTRIDGE PACKET LABELS: ⓐ , .54 cal. Merrill carbine, Richmond Arsenal; ⓑ , .44 cal. Colt Army, Richmond Arsenal; ⓒ , .36 cal. Colt Navy, Richmond Arsenal; ⓓ , .52 cal. Sharps rifle, Richmond Arsenal; ⓔ , 50 Musket Caps, Richmond Arsenal.

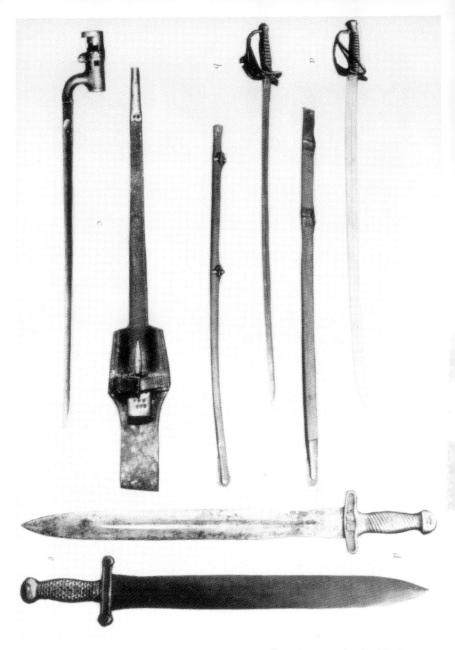

Plate 25. — ⓐ, cavalry sabre with wooden scabbard; ⓑ, infantry sword and scabbard, CSA in hilt; ⓒ, Enfield bayonet, scabbard and frog; ⓓ and ⓔ, artillery short swords.

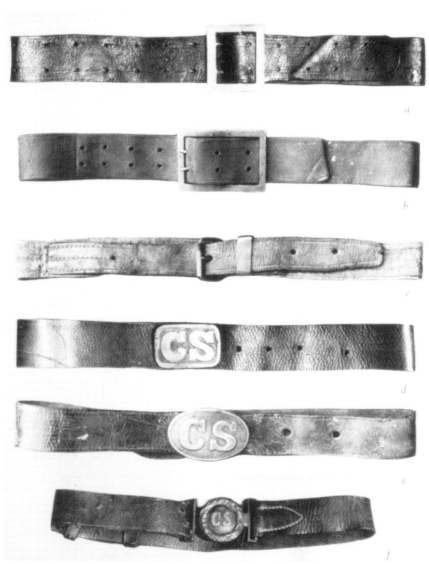

Plate 26.— ⓐ, "frame" buckle with belt; ⓑ, "wishbone" buckle with belt; ⓒ, "roller" buckle with leather and tarred canvas belt; ⓓ, rectangular C.S. buckle with belt; ⓔ, oval C.S. buckle with belt; ⓕ, 2-piece interlocking C.S. buckle with sabre belt (missing straps).

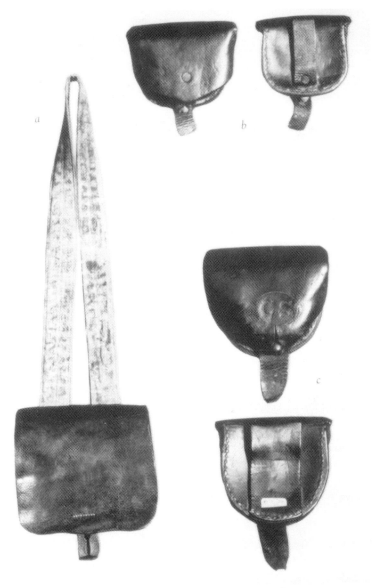

Plate 27.— ⓐ , infantry cartridge box with tarred canvas belt; ⓑ , cap pouch, reverse shows typical C.S. one belt loop construction; ⓒ , same, embossed "CS."

Plate 28.— (a) , embossed "CS" infantry cartridge box with belt; (b) , cavalry carbine cartridge box; (c) , tin "drum" canteen, embossed "CS."

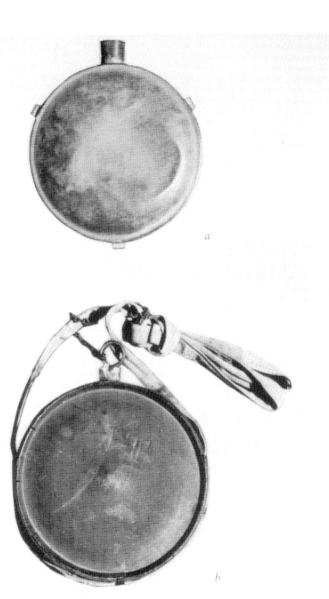

Plate 29.— ⓐ , tin "drum" canteen; ⓑ , wooden canteen with strap.

Plate 30.— ⓐ , friction primers, Richmond Arsenal; ⓑ , primer from *a*; ⓒ , primer, variant; ⓓ , lanyard; ⓔ , priming wire.

Plate 31.— ⓐ , 5-second time fuzes, Richmond Arsenal, one specimen removed from package; ⓑ , same, 2 seconds; ⓒ , assortment of Confederate paper time fuzes.

Plate 32.— ⓐ , Bormann time fuze; ⓑ , paper time fuze plug for spherical ball; ⓒ , same, for conical shell; ⓓ , McEvoy fuze igniter for paper time fuzes (insert only); ⓔ , top view of c; ⓕ , Bormann fuze setter; ⓖ , Bormann fuze cutter.